Contents

About your qualification

This textbook supports learners studying the core units of the Foundation in Construction and Building Services Engineering (Level 2) qualification (Qualifications Wales).

What we refer to as 'the built environment' can be a fascinating area of study. What we easily take for granted around us can reveal important historical information, impressive technological achievements and ingenious ways of working when examined more closely, something this textbook will assist learners to do.

The core units of the qualification featured in this book provide a broad introduction to construction and the built environment and develop essential knowledge and understanding of the construction industry over six chapters. A key chapter includes important principles related to health and safety in the workplace and the welfare responsibilities of all workers on site.

The subject matter covered by the core units provides essential underpinning knowledge which forms a foundation that you can build on when progressively studying selected trade specialisms to complete the course. Subjects considered include:

- the buildings and structures that make up the built environment and how changes take place over time
- the trades, roles and careers in the construction and built-environment sector
- employability skills relevant to workplace situations
- how construction and the built environment affects social, economic and environmental sustainability
- the use and application of emerging technologies.

While study of the six core units of the qualification provides valuable insights and understanding of the construction and built-environment sector, selection of two trade specialism options gives you the opportunity to develop planning, performing and evaluating skills while undertaking tasks that are common to the chosen trades.

How your knowledge and skills will be assessed

The Foundation in Construction and Building Services Engineering (Level 2) qualification is assessed using three assessment methods.

- On-screen assessment – an externally-set question paper that will also be externally-marked. The question paper relates to the core units covered in this textbook. This forms 20% of the qualification grade.

- Practical project – an externally-set project that will be marked internally by assessors at the training centre, covering two trade areas. This forms 60% of the qualification grade.
- Guided discussion – an externally-set formal conversation that will be marked internally by assessors at the training centre. This forms 20% of the qualification grade.

The **on-screen assessment** is marked automatically, and the results will be received by the assessment/training centre on the same day the assessment takes place.

At the end of each chapter in this textbook, a range of multiple-choice questions is included to give you the opportunity to get familiar with the format of the exam. Look carefully at the way the questions are structured to get comfortable with this method of testing your knowledge.

The **practical project** assessment takes the form of specified trade activities that must meet stipulated standards for two trade areas and must be completed prior to undertaking the guided discussion.

The **guided discussion** is a planned, in-depth, formal conversation between an assessor and the learner. It is used as a way of assessing understanding and knowledge of complex subjects. It is more than just 'a chat' and can be especially helpful to a learner who finds written expression difficult.

Some examples of the way in which a guided discussion can be structured are provided at the end of several chapters. You should develop the habit of regularly conversing naturally with others about the subject matter you are studying. One of the best ways to make learning about a subject effective and long-lasting is to explain it to others in your own words. Try to do this often to prepare for the guided discussion.

Continuing your learning journey

The qualification provides the knowledge, understanding and skills for learners to undertake further study. This includes progression to the following qualifications:

- Progression in Construction Level 2 – City & Guilds
- Progression in Building Services Engineering Level 2 – EAL
- Construction Level 3 (trade area) – City & Guilds
- Building Services Engineering Level 3 (trade area) – EAL.

Achieving this qualification will give you a comprehensive understanding of the construction and built-environment sector, enabling you to make informed decisions about your own career ambitions and development.

Acknowledgements

From the publisher

The publisher would like to acknowledge the following lecturers for their insightful feedback on the manuscript:

- Mike Gashe, Plastering Lecturer, Coleg Menai
- Jeff Price, Brickwork Lecturer, Coleg Llandrillo
- Martyn Pearson, Lecturer in Brickwork, Coleg Cambria
- City & Guilds' anonymous endorsement reviewer.

The publisher would like to thank Jill Fairweather (Historic Environment Skills Manager, Cadw, Welsh Government) for her thoughtful and constructive comments on the manuscript. Cadw is the Welsh Government's historic environment service working for an accessible and well-protected historic environment for Wales. You can find out more about them on their website (https://cadw.gov.wales/) or, in the context of the topics covered in this book, in their comprehensive teaching resource, 'Understanding Traditional (pre-1919) and Historic Buildings for Construction and Built Environment Courses' (https://cadw. gov.wales/learn/education/teaching-resources/understanding-traditional-pre-1919-and-historic-buildings).

The publisher would also like to thank City & Guilds for permission to reuse artworks from their Bricklaying textbooks, 9780851933030 and 9780851932682.

This book contains public sector information licensed under the Open Government Licence v3.0.

From the author

I'm grateful to have been given the opportunity to work on a textbook covering the core units of the Qualifications Wales Level 2 Foundation in Construction and Building Services Engineering.

Thanks to Tom Stottor at Hodder Education for including me in the project and being so supportive throughout.

Thanks also to the team at Hodder who have succeeded in producing an attractive book that connects with the reader and is a valuable teaching and learning resource for use in the classroom.

In particular, I've benefited greatly from the suggestions and encouragement Matthew Sullivan has provided during the refinement of the manuscript.

Also, many thanks to Imogen Miles whose editing skills and attention to detail have blended a range of content together on the page with great effect.

When a new qualification is designed, it offers the opportunity to explore existing subject matter with a fresh approach, and that has been the goal when writing this textbook. The structure and content of this qualification give the opportunity to delve into subjects of real interest and value relating to the past, present and future, and I've thoroughly enjoyed writing a textbook to support learners in Wales.

About the author

The construction industry has been central to my working life over a long period. I have worked as a skilled tradesman, a supervisor and a site manager on projects ranging from small extensions to multi-storey contracts worth millions of pounds. For a number of years, I employed a small team of skilled workers in my own construction company, working on prestige contracts for selected customers.

The skills I developed over the years allowed me to design and build my own family home in beautiful rural Wales, which I have always viewed as a highlight of my construction career. Relatively few people are able to have that privilege, and it was a particular pleasure to be able to achieve it in such an inviting part of the country.

After over 30 years working in various roles on construction sites, I was fortunate to move into the education sector, first as an NVQ trainer and assessor for three years and subsequently as a college lecturer. I worked for ten years in the Brickwork section at Cardiff and Vale College in South Wales where I taught bricklaying and other construction skills and became section leader.

Since leaving my college post, I have maintained my links with training and education, producing teaching and learning resources for City & Guilds along with my work as a technical author writing bricklaying and construction-related textbooks. I am pleased to be currently involved in the writing, reviewing and editing of resources for craft and trade qualification examinations.

Working in the construction industry followed by my work in the education sector has been very rewarding. My aim during my time teaching others has been to impart to learners the great job satisfaction that can be gained from becoming a skilled practitioner. Put maximum effort into developing your skills and knowledge, and you will be able to take full advantage of career opportunities that come your way.

Mike Jones, 2021

Picture credits

The Publishers would like to thank the following for permission to reproduce copyright material.

Fig.1.1 © Paul Wishart/Shutterstock.com; Fig.1.2 © Justin Kase zsixz/Alamy Stock Photo; Fig.1.3 © Shuang Li/stock.adobe.com; Fig.1.4 © Ceri Breeze/Shutterstock.com; Fig.1.5 © Creativenature.nl/stock.adobe.com; Fig.1.6 © Travelwitness/stock.adobe.com; Fig.1.7 © Carl DeAbreu/123 RF.com; Fig.1.8 © Allan Cash Picture Library/Alamy Stock Photo; Fig.1.9 © Johndavidphoto/123 RF.com; Fig.1.10 © Sebastien Coell/123 RF.com; Table 1.1 (top to bottom): © Philip Bird/123 RF.com, Steve Hughes Photography, © Cliff Day/Shutterstock.com, © Realimage/Alamy Stock Photo, © Nick Maslen/Alamy Stock Photo; Fig.1.11 © Travel/Alamy Stock Photo; Fig.1.12 © Vicky Jirayu/Shutterstock.com; Table 1.2 (top to bottom): © AberCPC/Alamy Stock Photo, © Billy Stock/Shutterstock.com, © Alan Morris/123 RF.com; Fig.1.13 © Wozzie/Shutterstock.com; Fig.1.14 © XtravaganT/stock.adobe.com; Fig.1.15 © Travelwitness/stock.adobe.com; Table 1.4 (top to bottom): © Jaroslaw Kilian/123 RF.com, © Roman Babakin/stock.adobe.com, © Bernd Brueggemann/stock.adobe.com, © Svensnulem/stock.adobe.com; Fig.1.16 © Karel Miragaya/123 RF.com; Fig.1.17 © Gav Smith/Shutterstock.com; Fig.1.18 Cardiff Libraries / Llyfrgelloedd Caerdydd; Fig.1.19 © LianeM/stock.adobe.com; Fig.1.20 Reprinted with permission from Encyclopædia Britannica, © 2014 by Encyclopædia Britannica, Inc.; Fig.1.21 © Billy Stock/Shutterstock.com; Fig.1.22 © Travellight/Shutterstock.com; Fig.1.23 Reprinted with permission from Encyclopædia Britannica, © 2014 by Encyclopædia Britannica, Inc.; Fig.1.24 © ThamKC/stock.adobe.com; Fig.1.25 © An-T/stock.adobe.com; Figs.1.26 and 1.27 Reprinted with permission from Encyclopædia Britannica, © 2014 by Encyclopædia Britannica, Inc.; Fig.1.28 © Lukassek/stock.adobe.com; Fig.1.29 Reprinted with permission from Encyclopædia Britannica, © 2014 by Encyclopædia Britannica, Inc.; Fig.1.30 © Morris71/123 RF.com; Fig.1.31 © PR images/Alamy Stock Photo; Fig.1.32 © Phillip Roberts/Alamy Stock Photo; Fig.1.33 © Avalon/Construction Photography/Alamy Stock Photo; Fig.1.34 © Maurice Savage/Alamy Stock Photo; Fig.1.35 © Alan1951/stock.adobe.com; Table 1.5 (top to bottom): © Jim Laws/Alamy Stock Photo, © Peter Cripps/123 RF.com, © Simon Cole/Alamy Stock Photo, © B.Panupong/Shutterstock.com, ©

Alex Daniels/Shutterstock.com; Table 1.6 (top to bottom): © Adrian Zenz/Shutterstock.com, © Paul needs/EyeEm/stock.adobe.com, © Jax10289/Shutterstock.com, © Martin Cooke/Alamy Stock Photo; Table 2.1 (top to bottom): © Martincp/stock.adobe.com, © Kevin Britland/Alamy Stock Photo, © Cryptographer/Shutterstock.com, © Ashley Cooper pics/Alamy Stock Photo; Table 2.2 (top to bottom): © Christopher Dodge/stock.adobe.com, © Highwaystarz/stock.adobe.com, © Auremar/stock.adobe.com, © Bilanol/stock.adobe.com; Table 2.3 (top to bottom): © Angela Hampton Picture Library/Alamy Stock Photo, © Simon Turner/Alamy Stock Photo, © Avalon/Construction Photography/Alamy Stock Photo, © Andrii Anna photographers/Shutterstock.com, © Auremar/stock.adobe.com; Table 2.5 (top to bottom): © Nik/stock.adobe.com, © U. J. Alexander/stock.adobe.com; Table 2.7 (top to bottom): © Lovethephoto/Alamy Stock Photo, © Andy Ginns/stock.adobe.com; Table 2.8 (top to bottom): © Jeff Morgan 13/Alamy Stock Photo, © Convery flowers/Alamy Stock Photo, © Travelib/Alamy Stock Photo; Fig.2.1 © Chris Pearsall/Alamy Stock Photo; Fig.2.2 © Artursfoto/stock.adobe.com; Fig.2.3 © Ungvar/stock.adobe.com; Table 2.14 (top to bottom): © Fotosearch/Getty Images, © Stieberszabolcs/123RF.com, © James Hadley/Alamy Stock Photo; Fig.2.4 © Sarah Smith/PA Images/Alamy Stock Photo; Fig.2.5 © Yackers1/Shutterstock.com; Fig.3.2 © MichaelGrant/Alamy Stock Photo; Table 3.2 (top to bottom): © Bannafarsai/stock.adobe.com, © 123RF, © Roman_23203/stock.adobe.com, © Estan Cabigas/Alamy Stock Photo, © Chad McDermott/stock.adobe.com; Fig.3.3 © Will Pryce/Arcaid Images/Alamy Stock Photo; Fig.3.5 © Apidachjsw/stock.adobe.com; Fig.3.10 © Geraint Nicholas/Shutterstock.com; Fig.3.11 © Jenny Thompson/stock.adobe.com; Table 3.6 top © EnVogue_Photo/Alamy Stock Photo; Fig.3.14 IG Lintels; Fig.3.19 © Paul eccleston/Alamy Stock Photo; Fig.3.26 © SteF/stock.adobe.com; Fig.3.27 © Kasipat/stock.adobe.com; Fig.3.29 © Rawpixel.com/stock.adobe.com; Fig.3.30 © Renamarie/stock.adobe.com; Fig.3.31 © trgowanlock/stock.adobe.com; Fig.3.32 © Paul Watkins Creative Photgraphy/Alamy Stock Photo; Fig.3.33 Image courtesy of Avongard.com; Fig.3.34 © Sakda2527/stock.adobe.com; Fig.3.35 © Jane/stock.adobe.com; Fig.3.36 © Mr.Smith Chetanachan/123RF.com; Fig.3.38 © Highwaystarz/stock.adobe.com; Fig.3.39 © Lois GoBe/

How to use this book

Throughout the book you will see the following features.

INDUSTRY TIP

It is good practice to alternate a task involving vibration with other work.

Industry tips are particularly useful pieces of advice that can assist you in your workplace or help you remember something important.

KEY TERM

Viaduct: a long bridge structure, constructed as a series of arches, carrying a road or railway across a valley or depression in the landscape

Key terms, marked in bold purple in the text, are explained to aid your understanding. (They are also explained in the Glossary at the back of the book.)

HEALTH AND SAFETY

Dense concrete blocks are heavy and need to be handled with care, using correct techniques.

Health and safety boxes provide important points to ensure safety in the workplace.

ACTIVITY

Search online for 'masonry footings'. Is this type of masonry constructed above ground or below ground?

Activities help to test your understanding.

Improve your maths items provide opportunities to practise or improve your maths skills.

Improve your English items provide opportunities to practise or improve your English skills.

Test your knowledge questions appear at the end of each chapter. These are designed to identify any areas where you might need further training or revision. Answers are provided at the back of the book.

Guided discussion questions appear at the end of most chapters. These are designed to replicate the guided discussion element of the assessment.

CHAPTER 1

INTRODUCTION TO THE BUILT ENVIRONMENT

INTRODUCTION

The term 'built environment' refers to anything constructed by humans to support human activity. To feel safe and comfortable, we depend on structures that have been built for us to live, learn and work in, as well as hospitals to provide healthcare and other facilities to protect us. The built environment also includes '**infrastructure**' in the form of travel systems, energy-distribution systems, water supplies and waste-disposal systems.

In this chapter, you will learn about the purpose and design of different structures and systems, and how they have changed over time.

LEARNING OUTCOMES

By the end of this chapter, you will:
1 understand the types and purposes of buildings in the built environment
2 know the different types of structures in the built environment.

1 BUILDINGS IN THE BUILT ENVIRONMENT

It is easy to take for granted just how essential buildings are in our lives. Our daily existence and the activities we engage in can be greatly affected by:

- the design features of buildings
- the shape and size of buildings
- the different purposes for which we use buildings.

1.1 Types of building

In this section, we will consider two types of building – domestic and public. In this context, 'domestic' refers to homes that individuals, couples or families live in. 'Public' refers to buildings that relate to or affect a population or community as a whole.

Domestic buildings

Buildings designed for domestic use, that is buildings we live in, can be referred to as dwellings. In Wales, we are all familiar with dwellings constructed as houses, bungalows and apartments.

Houses and bungalows can be:

- built as free-standing units, known as **detached properties**
- joined in pairs to form **semi-detached properties**
- linked together in rows, referred to as **terraced properties**.

▲ Figure 1.1 Detached house

▲ Figure 1.2 Semi-detached bungalow

KEY TERMS

Detached properties: stand-alone buildings that do not share any walls with other properties

Semi-detached properties: two buildings joined together on one side by a shared (party) wall

Terraced properties: similar buildings joined together in a row by the side (or party) walls

Detached dwellings standing alone on a plot can take up a considerable amount of land. This can make them more expensive for a construction company or developer to build, which can, in turn, increase the purchase cost to the buyer. Advantages of a detached house or bungalow include no direct noise or disturbance from neighbours and greater privacy for the occupants.

ACTIVITY

Look for bungalows in your local area that have projecting windows built into the roof structure. These are called 'dormer' bungalows.

While some dormer windows are constructed as part of the original design, it is often the case that owners have converted the attic into additional living space and added dormer windows.

By joining two properties together as semi-detached homes:

- less land is required
- material costs can be reduced, as the properties share a wall (known as a party wall)
- the number of properties that can be built on a development plot can be increased considerably by careful planning of the site layout.

Of course, joining two properties together increases the likelihood of noise transmission from one dwelling to the other.

In the past, terraced properties were built in large cities as ornate townhouses for wealthy owners. Designs in the seventeenth century often copied the style of fashionable European houses.

IMPROVE YOUR ENGLISH

Research 'Carlton House Terrace' online. Write a short report on who designed this structure, the style in which it was built and the sort of people who lived there.

In the nineteenth century, smaller terraced houses became popular as cheap accommodation for the working classes, especially in places like the South Wales Valleys during the development of the coal industry. Long terraces were built following the curves of the mountainous landscape, and many of these dwellings have been modernised and are still in use today.

▲ Figure 1.3 Seventeenth-century terraced houses

▲ Figure 1.4 Terraced houses in the South Wales Valleys

Modern terraced houses are often referred to as 'link houses' and benefit from improved design features and construction materials to insulate against sound transmission between dwellings.

Over time, due to the increasing cost of purchasing land for development, the construction of multi-storey dwellings in the form of apartments (or flats) has become increasingly common. Far more homes can be constructed on a small plot of land by literally stacking one home on top of another.

Modern apartments are often designed with attractive features and located in interesting and convenient locations, such as regenerated dockland areas in cities like Cardiff and Swansea.

▲ Figure 1.5 Modern terraced houses

▲ Figure 1.6 Apartment blocks in regenerated docklands

Some people prefer to live in smaller homes called chalets, and these are often grouped together in a residential park or estate. This type of dwelling tends to be relatively simple in design and construction, and therefore operating and maintenance costs are reduced.

Public buildings

Some public buildings are used frequently by large numbers of people, while others are used only occasionally and for specific purposes. The way they are intended to be used will have an effect on the design.

For example, school, college and university buildings are used frequently by large numbers of individuals, almost on a daily basis throughout most of the year. Additionally, they may be used occasionally by the community, as locations for activities not connected with education. For example, they could be used as polling stations or meeting places for other specific public events.

By contrast, places of worship may only be used at weekends or on infrequent occasions throughout the week by a limited number of people. The design of buildings such as these can allow for flexibility in the number of users by including movable walls or screens to adapt the size of room spaces.

Other public buildings operate as workplaces for those offering specific services to the community. For example, personnel working in a police station undertake law-enforcement activities to protect the community. Buildings that operate as police stations are specifically designed to offer office space for administration and document processing, interview rooms, detention facilities, and often garage space for police vehicles.

▲ Figure 1.7 Cardiff Central Police Station

An extensive range of public buildings is essential to the efficient operation of organised society, for example:

- hospitals to provide community healthcare
- courts and prisons to support law-enforcement agencies
- buildings to accommodate local and central government administration.

ACTIVITY

Discuss with a partner the design features required in the following buildings:

- hospitals
- courts
- prisons.

For each type of building, list the features they might need in order to function efficiently.

Public buildings that form part of the built environment are used for a broad range of purposes, and it not possible to discuss every type of building here.

As mentioned above, the design features of any public building will be influenced by its intended purpose and its location in the built environment. Later in this chapter, we will discuss how the design of a building must take into account how those using it are affected by the shape of rooms, the light entering the structure and the space available. For example, a library will be designed to provide quiet spaces for reading and browsing literature that is stored in an orderly manner.

Some public buildings have unique design features that are specific to their purpose and will not be found in any other context, such as the following.

- In towns and cities where industry or manufacturing was a key employer, the range of public buildings commonly included gathering places for workers (formerly referred to as 'working men's institutes' and now often known as 'social clubs'). These buildings typically featured a small auditorium for entertainment events, lounge areas with a bar for socialising, a reading room and, in some cases, changing rooms where sports facilities were part of the provision.
- A railway station must have precisely designed platforms at specific height levels and distances from the railway track to allow passengers to safely access the trains. Other structures within the station complex provide areas for ticket sales, sheltered waiting areas, food sales outlets, toilet facilities and designated spaces for staff and railway workers.

▲ Figure 1.8 A working men's institute in the 1970s

▲ Figure 1.9 Flint railway station

1.2 Key construction design areas and changes over time

The modern built environment is a complex collection of building designs and structures that have evolved over generations to support human activity. Let's identify the key areas of change that have taken place in the design of public buildings.

Up to the 1950s

Architectural design and types of construction are often categorised as belonging to a distinctive time period or **era**, named according to the king or queen reigning at that time. For example, the Victorian era is named after Queen Victoria, who reigned from 1837 to 1901.

Earlier building designs were often noted for their ornate decorative features and grand appearance. Public buildings from the Victorian era up to the 1950s are sometimes referred to as 'statement' buildings, because they were designed to look impressive and to add to the prestige of a town or city.

A distinctive example is the Pierhead Building located at Cardiff Bay. It was constructed in 1897 as the headquarters of the Bute Dock Company, which had a key role in wealth generation for the city. The design incorporates what are referred to as Gothic architectural features. The building became the administrative office for the Port of Cardiff in 1947 and now serves the public as a Welsh history museum and exhibition centre.

KEY TERM

Era: a period of time distinguished by particular characteristics

▲ Figure 1.10 Pierhead Building, Cardiff Bay

ACTIVITY

Research the Cardiff Pierhead Building online. Choose three of its many decorative features and copy and paste images of them into a Microsoft Word document. Write next to each image how you think creating the feature might impact on the:

- cost of constructing the building
- time required to construct the building
- ongoing maintenance costs.

The considerable cost of constructing public buildings with ornate **classical** features meant that funding had to come from government or, alternatively, from wealthy individuals who wanted to benefit the community (referred to as **philanthropists**).

▼ Table 1.1 Key design features before the mid-twentieth century

Year	Design features	Example
1550	• Stone used for durability • Some brick in use • Many building designs similar to traditional **medieval** styles • Some structures built with heavy timber frames	 ▲ Abernodwydd Farmhouse
1650	• Stone still used extensively • Building skills training improving in the crafts of joinery and brickwork • Greater use of decorative features	 ▲ Bodysgallen Hall, Llandudno
1750	• Use of **dressed stone** to produce complex decorative features • Stone tiles used for roof coverings, as well as slate	 ▲ Margam Orangery, Port Talbot

KEY TERMS

Classical: following a traditional and long-established style; terms such as 'classical Greek' can be applied to architecture

Philanthropist: a person who benefits others, especially by the generous donation of money to good causes

Medieval: relating to the Middle Ages, a time period from about the fifth century to the late fifteenth century

Dressed stone: natural stone that has been cut and shaped to the required size, shape and finish

ACTIVITY

Visit https://cadw.gov.
wales/learn/education/
teaching-resources/
understanding-traditional-
pre-1919-and-historic-
buildings to access Cadw
and Historic England's
teaching resource,
'Understanding Traditional
(pre-1919) and Historic
Buildings for Construction
and Built Environment
Courses'.

Read pages 7–9 of the
document to see how the
architectural components
of a building have
changed over time.

▼ Table 1.1 Key design features before the mid-twentieth century (continued)

Year	Design features	Example
1850	• Greater use of brick and stucco, which is a smooth coating applied over masonry to create decorative effects • Sophisticated designs more common • Technological advances see the increasing use of innovative materials such as iron, larger panes of glass and concrete • Shift from local to mass-produced materials	▲ Glynllifon Mansion, Llandwrog
1950	• Solid wall construction replaced by cavity walls • Reconstruction after the Second World War requiring faster building methods • Simpler architectural approach • Late nineteenth-/early twentieth-century use of corrugated iron for roofs, especially in small churches	▲ Pola Cinema, Welshpool

Buildings from this time period are often described as 'historic' or 'traditional'. They used construction methods and materials in different ways. It is important to bear these original methods and materials in mind when working on traditional buildings.

From the 1950s onwards

Public buildings from the mid-1950s onwards have largely moved away from complex and elaborate designs, which had a greater focus on the **aesthetic** value of the building. Modern designs often give more emphasis to **functional** efficiency.

Many public buildings constructed in the 1960s and 1970s have been described as tasteless in appearance, due to this noticeable shift away from the richly decorated buildings of the past, which used ornate designs and costly materials. Instead, structures using concrete panels in repetitive geometric shapes and patterns became common in many towns and cities.

This architectural style, often referred to as 'brutalism', led to quicker completion of projects and reduced the reliance on highly skilled craftsmen. The resulting potential cost savings were a factor in encouraging private investors to take the place of the government in funding many projects. Lots of public buildings designed in this manner are still in use and are easy to identify.

Modern-day public buildings are often designed with outer walls that consist of sleek glass and lightweight metal units (referred to as 'curtain walling'), which further speeds up construction and makes the interior of the building lighter and more pleasant for the users. In addition, these units can be manufactured from materials that save energy by preventing heat transfer in and out of the building.

KEY TERMS

Aesthetic: concerned with beauty and good taste; relating to the appreciation of beauty

Functional: designed to be practical and useful, rather than attractive

ACTIVITY

Search online for 'curtain walling'. List the range of materials that can be used to manufacture curtain walling and then outline the advantages of using this system.

▲ Figure 1.11 An example of brutalism: the former County Hall in Mold, Flintshire

▲ Figure 1.12 An example of curtain walling: Cardiff Central Library

▼ Table 1.2 Key design features after the mid-twentieth century

Year	Design features	Example
1960	<ul><li>Cavity walls constructed in masonry giving way to a range of materials, including structural steel frames and reinforced concrete</li><li>Larger internal spaces offering flexibility</li></ul>	▲ University of Wales, Aberystwyth
1980	<ul><li>New materials and ideas expressed in architecture</li><li>Many attractive building designs making use of new technologies and manufacturing techniques</li><li>New methods of glass manufacturing, allowing imaginative design</li></ul>	▲ National Botanic Garden of Wales, Llanarthney
2000	<ul><li>Renewed emphasis on 'statement' buildings for public use</li><li>Striking use of local materials</li><li>Greater consideration of environmental impact throughout the working life of a building</li></ul>	▲ Wales Millennium Centre, Cardiff

Future design considerations

The design of public buildings for the fast-moving modern world must take into account the need for rapid communication. This has led to many buildings being constructed close to transport networks away from the centre of towns and cities.

A sustainable built environment depends on using **renewable** energy sources in new buildings, such as wind turbines, solar panels, and heat pumps that extract heat from the ground or the air and transfer it into the building. This, coupled with the increasing use of materials that are sourced locally and produce less carbon in their manufacture, means that buildings for the future will bear little resemblance to buildings of the past.

Commercial and industrial buildings

A property used by a company or business to make a profit can be referred to as a commercial building.

Industrial buildings include factories used to manufacture products or process materials and warehouses used as distribution centres or simply to store goods.

Like domestic and public buildings, the design and use of commercial and industrial buildings have also changed to suit the needs of society. Table 1.3 outlines some of these changes.

> **KEY TERM**
>
> **Renewable:** from natural sources or processes that are replenished or replaced

▼ Table 1.3 Changes in the way commercial and industrial buildings are used

Purpose of building	Type of building	Changes in use over time
Retail	Commercial	In the past, buildings used for retail commercial purposes ranged from corner shops, which were conveniently located within the community, to high street department stores in town and city centres. While convenience stores still serve the community, town centre shopping must now compete with retail parks located in the outskirts of (or even beyond) towns and cities with direct links to transport hubs. Supermarkets have increased considerably in size since their introduction to the UK in the 1970s.
Bank	Commercial	High street banks used to be a prominent feature of town centres, as well as popular locations in the suburbs, often housed within ornate buildings that gave an impression of importance and status. With the move to online banking and the reduced need to visit bank branches in an increasingly cashless society, many bank branches have closed. The buildings that remain have been used for a variety of purposes, such as conversion into pubs, apartments and offices.
Office	Commercial	Small offices located in a variety of locations, such as rooms above high street shops, still serve the needs of small businesses. Offices for large businesses have increased in scale and number in important city locations. Many large companies use office complexes that are arranged in centralised blocks with other large companies. Business parks have become a feature on the outskirts of many towns and cities, providing working spaces for businesses of varying sizes that are conveniently located near transport networks.

▼ Table 1.3 Changes in the way commercial and industrial buildings are used (continued)

Purpose of building	Type of building	Changes in use over time
Leisure	Commercial	Leisure facilities have long been provided by local councils to serve the community on a non-profit basis, arranged so that users simply cover the cost of operations. However, commercial leisure businesses have increased in number over time, as health and fitness have become a priority for many. Multi-purpose facilities located centrally for office workers and in convenient locations within population centres have increased in number in recent years.
Warehouse	Industrial/commercial	Warehouse size and capacity has increased considerably over time due to a number of factors. With the increase in size of 'superstores', stock is transported to stores on a 'just in time' basis. This requires large warehouse facilities at locations that allow fast distribution to a number of stores. Another influencing factor is the growth of online shopping, which frequently offers next-day delivery. The range of goods on offer requires massive storage capacity to be maintained.
Factory	Industrial	Over time, the location of factory buildings for manufacturing and processing has been planned to take best advantage of the availability of workers and resources. Increasingly, small- to medium-sized factory buildings are located in industrial parks, where there are convenient links to transport networks and supply chains.
Agriculture	Industrial	Agricultural methods have evolved over time to greatly increase production levels. This has led to larger-scale operations, often involving specialist buildings such as huge greenhouses and buildings to house bulky, expensive equipment. In some cases, traditional buildings such as barns have become redundant and have been converted for use as homes or small offices.

The design of public, commercial and industrial buildings will develop and change to suit the future needs of society, especially with regard to the use of environmentally sustainable materials and construction methods.

The life cycle of new buildings must also be carefully planned to make sure that environmental damage is minimised or prevented during use of the building over time. This will be discussed in greater detail in Chapter 3.

1.3 Cultural requirements for different buildings and structures

As mentioned earlier in this chapter, it is important that buildings such as libraries are designed to create a pleasant environment for the user, for example, through the shape of the rooms or by the careful use of space and light.

This is true for a number of special-use buildings, especially for those that serve **cultural** needs such as museums, art galleries and places of worship.

Museums and art galleries are designed as places to educate visitors and satisfy their curiosity by displaying items of value or interest in an engaging way. Therefore, it is important that the building design allows for adequate lighting in display areas. The planned use of space can create a calm environment that puts visitors at ease and encourages them to linger in selected areas of interest.

KEY TERM

Cultural: connected with the customs, ideas and behaviours of a society

▲ Figure 1.13 National Library of Wales in Aberystwyth

Both these types of building may be required to support the conservation of valuable items or **artifacts**. The building design will therefore need to include specialist storage and restoration facilities. Also, many museums and galleries are housed in buildings that are designed to impress the visitor with their grand scale and decorative design.

Places of worship, such as churches, chapels, cathedrals, mosques and temples, are typically designed to create a deep and lasting impression on visitors, due to their imposing size and magnificent appearance. Their spacious interiors, together with the clever use of light, are intended to produce a sense of awe and reverence in those who use the buildings.

Similar principles may be applied to the design of civic buildings, such as city halls and other governmental administration buildings. Impressive building designs can encourage respect and esteem for the authority they represent.

KEY TERM

Artifacts: ornaments or other objects made by humans that are of cultural or historical interest

▲ Figure 1.14 Light entering a place of worship can create an impressive effect

▲ Figure 1.15 City Hall, Cardiff

1.4 Societal requirements for communities

While buildings can be designed to fulfil the specific needs of individuals or groups of individuals within the community, how those buildings are set out and arranged in relation to each other can also affect how the needs of a community are met.

For example, if schools were located too far away from transport links or the dwellings of pupils and staff, the school community would be adversely affected and function less efficiently.

When planning the built environment, it is important to take into account the social and cultural needs of the community across a range of requirements, such as the following.

- The whole of the built environment must be accessible to all, including those with impaired or reduced mobility.
- The built environment must be designed and planned with safety in mind, making sure that transport systems function effectively without harm to those living and working within the community.
- The practical necessity for easy access to all parts of the community must be balanced with the need to provide security for all within that community.

These factors are assessed and incorporated into local development plans formulated by local government. The aim is to integrate transport links with areas of high social demand and segregate areas for domestic use from commercial and industrial activity.

ACTIVITY

How close is your home to places of education, shops, leisure facilities and places of worship? List the buildings mentioned that are within two miles of your home. Which are further away?

Local government officers also apply national building regulations, to make sure that all buildings and structures that make up the built environment are constructed to safe standards, in accordance with approved established methods and practices.

2 STRUCTURES IN THE BUILT ENVIRONMENT

Infrastructure is a major part of a successful built environment. Remember, infrastructure was defined at the beginning of this chapter as the basic systems and services that a country or organisation needs in order to function properly.

There are different types of infrastructure that work alongside each other to service the many needs of the community:

- transport – including road, rail, air and water
- services – including electricity, gas and drainage
- flood and coastal defences
- communications – including internet, telephone, television and radio.

These elements of infrastructure can be large-scale projects that literally involve 'moving mountains', referred to as civil engineering.

2.1 Types of infrastructure

Transport

Road transport

Roads and highways allow members of a community to interact with one another and travel to work, school or leisure facilities. Obtaining food and other everyday essentials depends more and more on efficient local road networks, whether we shop in person or have items we have purchased delivered to our homes.

Table 1.4 describes different types of UK roads and highways that form part of our infrastructure.

▼ Table 1.4 Types of UK roads and highways

Type of road or highway	Description
Motorway  ▲ A busy motorway	Motorways are major roads built specifically for fast travel over long distances. All motorways have a minimum of two lanes in each carriageway (known as dual carriageway), and in busy regions they may have more than two lanes to handle the volume of traffic. They are designed with special entry points, where vehicles can safely merge with fast-moving traffic. Exit points are designed to allow vehicles to safely reduce speed to levels suitable for non-motorway traffic. Direction signs are usually blue with white text and route names are numbered, for example, M4 or M1.
A-road  ▲ An A-road through Snowdonia National Park	A-roads are major roads connecting towns and cities that are not motorways. Sometimes referred to as trunk roads, there are approximately 2,000 miles of A-roads in Wales, made up of both single and dual carriageway in rural and urban areas. A-roads have a mixture of junction arrangements, including entry/exit points and roundabouts. Direction signs are usually green with white text and route names are numbered, for example, A48 or A470.
B-road  ▲ A typical B-road	B-roads are minor roads that have a single carriageway. Some only have a single lane with passing places. They link small towns and villages and can offer alternative routes to busy roads for enjoying a slower pace and appreciating scenery or points of special interest. Direction signs are usually white with black text and route names are numbered, for example, B4347.

▼ Table 1.4 Types of UK roads and highways (continued)

Type of road or highway	Description
Cycle path  ▲ Cycle paths may be shared with pedestrians	Cycle paths are for bicycle use only, with clear segregation from cars and other vehicles. If they are shared with pedestrians, pathway markings may be provided to indicate where each class of user should travel.

Rail transport

Railways are a vital part of infrastructure, allowing the:

- safe transport of heavy or bulky goods and materials
- mass movement of people.

Around many major towns and cities, a large proportion of the working population relies on efficient rail transport to get them to employment centres and home again.

Building a rail network requires significant financial investment. Railway construction was at its peak in Wales during the nineteenth century, when many railways were built to transport coal from South Wales and slate from North Wales, creating great wealth that rewarded those who had paid the construction costs.

▲ Figure 1.16 Railways are a vital part of infrastructure

Later, tourism increased and railways were used to serve resorts such as Barry Island in the south and Llandudno in the north.

Moving people from place to place is still an important use of rail infrastructure and investment in modernising the rail network is substantial. For example, the electrification of the Great Western Railway route from Cardiff to London was completed early in January 2020.

ACTIVITY

Research the electrification of the Great Western Railway route from Cardiff to London, considering the following questions.

- How much did the project cost?
- How long did the project take to complete?
- What unexpected problems arose during the project?

▲ Figure 1.17 Cardiff International Airport

Air transport

Infrastructure for air transport requires large areas of flat, level land without obstacles such as hills or mountains. The location is prepared with suitable runways and taxiways, terminal buildings, housing for safety and emergency services, and facilities for air-traffic control. The international airport for Cardiff was developed from a former air-force training base constructed in the 1940s. Over time it has expanded significantly, and in 2019 it was used by more than 1.6 million passengers, who benefitted from the modernised and extended facilities.

There are many smaller airports and airstrips across Wales that provide for light aircraft operations and support private pilot-training schools.

Water transport

Before the construction of the railway network, movement of heavy materials over long distances was achieved using canals. These were constructed through the hilly terrain of Wales to provide reliable transport of coal and other heavy materials to factories for manufacturing and to ports for export.

Today, what remains of the thousands of miles of canals constructed across the UK are used mainly for leisure and holiday purposes. With the arrival of the railways, much of the canal system fell into disuse and many canals have been abandoned or filled in.

ACTIVITY

Visit www.historypoints.org and search for 'site of Glamorganshire Canal'. Find out the route that the canal took through Cardiff before it was filled in. Note how the sections of the canal near its end were wide enough to allow large ships to use it.

Many canal systems carried goods to coastal ports. This required the creation of structures to permit convenient loading and unloading of cargo. The construction of quays, docks and piers often involved significant civil engineering work, excavating large areas to form water basins deep enough to contain the vessels using them and allowing connections to road and rail transport systems.

▲ Figure 1.18 The Glamorganshire Canal carried cargo to the port of Cardiff

Managing obstacles in the landscape

Over time, transport systems using road, rail and water have carried millions of tons of goods over thousands of miles. In many cases, the routes of these systems have to cross hills and valleys, requiring a range of structures to be built to establish a safe and relatively level passage. Let's look at some of the structures that carry roads, railways and, in some cases, canals over and under obstacles in the landscape.

Bridges

In early human history, bridges over short distances were simple structures consisting of little more than tree trunks laid across a ditch or trench. Today, bridge designs have evolved to become highly technical structures carrying high volumes of road and rail traffic over great distances.

Arch bridges

Arch bridges are one of the oldest types of bridge. The Romans are famous for their arched structures, some of which are still in use after thousands of years.

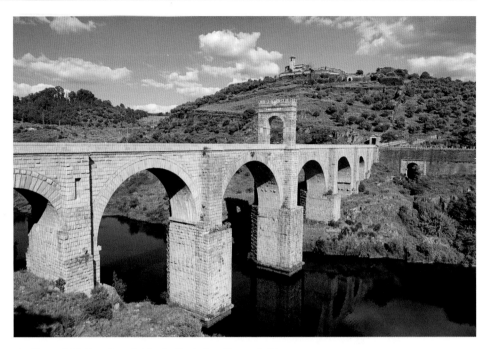

▲ Figure 1.19 Alcantara Bridge in Spain is a Roman bridge

The weight of traffic passing over an arched bridge is transferred around the radius of the arch to the piers (or abutments) at each end, and then down to the supporting foundations.

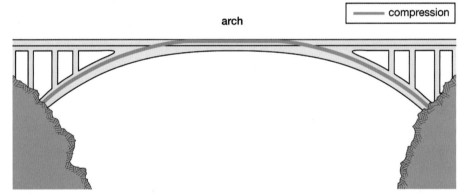

▲ Figure 1.20 How an arched bridge transmits loadings

In order to cross longer distances, a number of arches can be used, supported by evenly spaced piers across the span.

Many arched structures can be seen in the form of railway bridges constructed in brick, often referred to as **viaducts**. Similar structures that carry water are referred to as **aqueducts**.

KEY TERMS

Viaduct: a long bridge structure, constructed as a series of arches, carrying a road or railway across a valley or depression in the landscape

Aqueduct: an artificial channel in the form of a bridge carrying water across a valley

▲ Figure 1.21 Monnow Bridge at Monmouth, Wales

▲ Figure 1.22 Pontcysyllte Aqueduct

Beam bridges

This is the most common form of bridge design. As you take a trip along any motorway, you will travel over and under numerous beam bridges.

The beams or girders in the structure transfer the loads to the piers supporting them. As weight is placed on the deck of the bridge, the beams supporting the deck bend slightly, creating **compressive forces** in the top of the beams and **tensional forces** in the bottom of the beams.

> **KEY TERMS**
>
> **Compressive force:** pressure against an object that causes it to become squeezed or squashed
>
> **Tensional force:** the force created by pulling something from either end

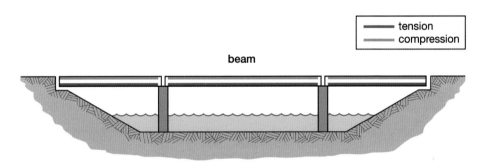

▲ Figure 1.23 A beam bridge

Many rail bridges are constructed using the beam design, with multiple concrete and steel beams arranged side by side to support the great weight of moving trains (see Figure 1.24).

Just as viaducts crossing a wide valley have piers spaced evenly to support a number of sections, beam bridges can be made up of multiple sections supported on a string of piers.

▲ Figure 1.24 Concrete bridge beams

Truss bridges

The truss design allows a heavy load to be carried by a bridge that contains a relatively small quantity of materials.

The horizontal members (beams) at the top of the truss deal with compressive forces, while the horizontal members at the bottom deal with tensional forces.

Figure 1.26 shows how other parts of the bridge manage the different forces created by the load it carries.

▲ Figure 1.25 A truss bridge

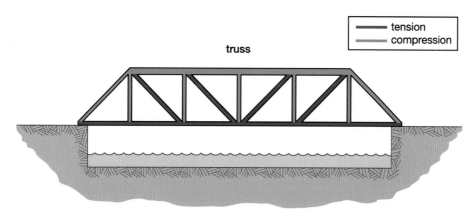

▲ Figure 1.26 How a truss bridge transmits loadings

Cantilever bridges

A **cantilever** bridge is essentially a combination of the beam and truss designs with some variations.

When constructed in three sections, the two outer sections have one end anchored to the end points of the span and the other end projecting out over the channel to be crossed. The two outer sections are centrally supported on piers, and the third central section rests on the projecting cantilevered arms of the outer sections. A similar arrangement would be a simple beam supported at its centre, with one end fixed and the other end stretching out over nothing.

> **KEY TERM**
>
> **Cantilever:** a projecting beam or structural member supported only at one end

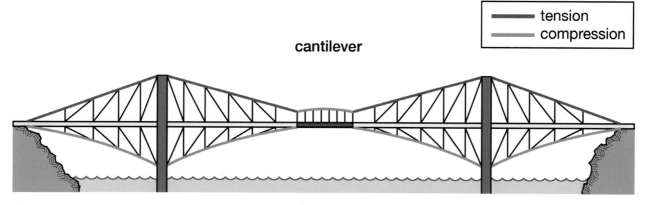

▲ Figure 1.27 A cantilever bridge

Perhaps the most famous cantilever bridge is the Forth Rail Bridge in Scotland (see Figure 1.28). This amazing structure has three cantilever sections with smaller sections spanning between them. Rather than anchoring the end points of each cantilever section to the shore, the massive sections rely on their balanced weight to support the smaller sections between them.

▲ Figure 1.28 The Forth Rail Bridge in Scotland

Suspension bridges

Suspension bridges carry loadings using cables attached to towers stretching across the full distance of the span. Additional cables are attached to the main cables and drop down vertically to support the deck of the bridge.

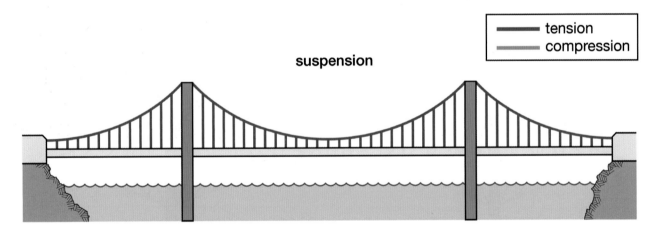

▲ Figure 1.29 A suspension bridge

The deck of the bridge is literally suspended in the air above the obstacle being crossed. It must be designed to be stable in high winds, since airflow from the side of the bridge can affect the deck like an aircraft wing, lifting it out of position and distorting its shape. Poorly designed suspension bridges have suffered catastrophic failure due to the effects of high winds.

The first bridge across the River Severn connecting England and Wales was a suspension bridge. It opened in 1966 and is still in use alongside the Second Severn Crossing, now renamed the Prince of Wales Bridge, which opened in 1996.

Tunnels

The routes of road, rail and canal transport systems sometimes require the use of tunnels where the landscape contains obstacles that cannot be bypassed. Like bridges, tunnel design and construction methods have become highly technical processes.

Bored tunnels

Bored tunnels are constructed using huge machines, logically referred to as 'tunnel boring machines' (TBMs).

'Full-face' or 'whole-face' TBMs can create large-diameter tunnels in hard rock, requiring very few workers. The debris created by the cutting operation is removed using conveyor belts. One of the world's largest TBMs is capable of cutting a tunnel 17.5 m (57.5 feet) in diameter.

After the TBM has cut out a specified length of tunnel which is unsupported, the tunnel must be lined, usually with concrete sections that are designed to resist the pressure of the material surrounding the excavation.

▲ Figure 1.30 A tunnel boring machine

▲ Figure 1.31 Concrete lining sections in place

Cut-and-cover tunnels

'Cut and cover' is a simple method of constructing shallow tunnels. A trench is excavated (or cut) along the line of the tunnel and the open top of the trench is covered over. If the intention is to build structures over the top of the tunnel, the cover must be able to support the loads imposed upon it.

An example of a cut-and-cover tunnel is the Queen's Gate Tunnel in Cardiff (see Figure 1.32). Originally, the A4232 trunk road was planned to be constructed at ground level. However, residents objected, stating that a surface road would physically split the local community in two, so the decision was taken to 'hide' the road in a tunnel, which is shallow enough to use the cut-and-cover construction method.

▲ Figure 1.32 The Queen's Gate Tunnel, Cardiff

Immersed-tube tunnels

This type of tunnel is installed in deep water. Sections of tunnel are manufactured on land, sealed so that they can be floated to the required location, and then flooded to sink them into position, usually in a shallow trench on the seabed or riverbed.

The section is then resealed and the water is pumped out. Further sections are added to create a continuous underwater route for roads or railways. The tunnel sections may be fully or partially covered, especially in the sea, to protect them from being damaged by ships passing above or by ships' anchors being dropped to the seabed.

▲ Figure 1.33 Sections of immersed-tube tunnel are manufactured on land

ACTIVITY

Find out where the nearest power station is to your home. What fuel does it use? How long has it been generating electricity?

Services

The services distribution network is very important in our everyday lives. If part of it stops working, we are likely to notice immediately.

It is easy to take for granted our electricity, gas and water supplies, since the methods of getting these services to our homes and workplaces are largely invisible. Cables and pipes are usually buried underground and out of sight.

We often only become aware of our electricity distribution system when we travel near power stations and see pylons carrying high-voltage cables to our towns and cities. Electricity is conducted to substations nearer to the point of use, where the **voltage** is progressively reduced to levels suitable for safe use by the consumer.

Gas is an important energy source; it fuels both domestic heating systems and many industrial and manufacturing processes. In the 1960s, with the discovery of natural gas beneath the seabed of the North Sea, a massive distribution network was modernised and extended to deliver this new type of gas nationally. Previously, 'town gas' was an energy source in the UK, which was produced by processing coal.

As North Sea gas diminishes, there is an increasing reliance on gas supplies brought into the UK by undersea pipelines from Europe and beyond. Liquified natural gas (LNG) is also imported into the country using specially designed tanker ships. A major port handling and storing LNG is located in Milford Haven in South West Wales.

▲ Figure 1.34 Discharging LNG from a tanker at Milford Haven

The use of both electricity and gas is being scrutinised more and more, with a view to making energy supplies secure and minimising damage to the environment.

- There is greater use of wind turbines and solar panels to supply energy, with large-scale installations referred to as 'energy farms'.
- Research is being undertaken to create electricity from wave power.
- Heating systems using energy from **biomass** are being improved.

Water is supplied to our homes and workplaces via a complex and extensive distribution system that requires constant maintenance and repair. If large water pipes or mains are damaged or broken, the resulting disruption and damage that can occur through flooding remind us of the huge volumes of processed water that modern society consumes.

Water stored in a **reservoir** or pumped from underground sources goes through a long process of purification, possibly travelling many miles before it arrives in our taps at home or at a manufacturing facility.

Artificial lakes that form reservoirs are often created by building a dam across a valley to retain rainwater. By releasing water in a controlled manner from a dam, it is possible to generate hydroelectric power, which is a renewable energy source.

KEY TERM

Voltage: the amount of potential energy between two points in an electrical circuit, expressed as volts or V

KEY TERMS

Biomass: organic matter used as a fuel, such as wood products, dried vegetation, crop residues, aquatic plants and even rubbish

Reservoir: a large natural or artificial lake used as a source of water supply

▲ Figure 1.35 A dam constructed to create a reservoir in the Elan Valley

KEY TERM

Storm water: water from heavy falls of rain or snow, or ice melt, that is not absorbed through the surface of the ground

Just as important as the systems bringing services to our homes and workplaces are the drainage systems that take away **storm water** and waste water for treatment or regulated safe disposal.

● Storm-water drainage must be carefully controlled to prevent flooding and ground saturation.
● Sewage must be treated in accordance with strict regulations before it can be discharged into a river or the sea.

Flood and coastal defences

With high levels of annual rainfall and many miles of coastline, flood and coastal defences are important elements of infrastructure in Wales.

Table 1.5 describes some types of flood defences.

▼ Table 1.5 Types of flood defences

Type	Description
Catchment areas	Catchment areas are often referred to as floodplains. As a river winds through a landscape, its volume varies according to the amount of rainfall upstream. A flat area extending from the banks of the river to the edge of the river valley provides a temporary catchment area, allowing safe expansion of the river volume. If the floodplain is altered or disturbed by human activity, such as constructing buildings on it, this can result in eventual flooding of the newly constructed buildings and of settlements at other locations along the river's path. ▲ A catchment area or floodplain

▼ Table 1.5 Types of flood defences (continued)

Type	Description	
Levees, bunds and weirs	Levees are embankments that stop a river overflowing. They can occur naturally as a river deposits sediment along its banks or they can be constructed artificially.	▲ Levees along a riverbank
	A bund is an embankment often created from earth and stone to control the flow of water in a similar way to a levee.	▲ A flood-control bund
	A weir is a low dam constructed across a river to alter the water level upstream or to regulate the general flow.	▲ A weir

▼ Table 1.5 Types of flood defences (continued)

Type	Description
Movable gates and barriers	To protect buildings from flood damage, a range of movable gates and barriers have been devised. These range from portable walls comprising sections of lightweight rigid material to inflatable tubes that seal openings in buildings' walls. ▲ Movable barriers protecting properties from flood damage

ACTIVITY

Discuss with a partner what could happen to underground drains in a flood situation. Could the contents of the drain be pushed back into a house? How could drainage systems and inspection chambers be protected? Write down your conclusions.

Table 1.6 describes different types of coastal defences.

▼ Table 1.6 Types of coastal defences

Type	Description
Groynes	Groynes are low walls that extend from the shore into the sea. They are used to stop erosion by interrupting the flow of the sea from side to side along a beach. ▲ Groynes on a Welsh beach
Sea wall	A sea wall protects the coast from erosion or damage. Since it must be able to withstand battering from waves, it must be an extremely sturdy structure. Generally, large quantities of heavy stones and concrete are used in the construction, leading to the description 'hard engineering'. ▲ A sea wall pounded by the sea at Porthcawl

▼ Table 1.6 Types of coastal defences (continued)

Type	Description	
Revetment	A revetment is a type of sea wall. However, instead of simply building it as strong as possible to physically resist the action of waves, a revetment is designed with a long sloping face to absorb the wave energy.	 ▲ A revetment in front of a sea wall
Gabion	A gabion is a large steel basket or cage placed in the required position and then filled with stones or rocks. Generally, several gabions will be used in combination to create a bulky barrier to prevent erosion by the action of waves or the flow of a river.	 ▲ Gabions protecting the bank of the River Teifi

With concern growing about the rate of climate change around the planet and predictions of significant rises in sea levels, flood and coastal defences will become an increasingly important element of infrastructure, protecting the rest of the built environment.

Communications

Infrastructure to support telecommunication services is complex and expensive to build and maintain. However, these services have become key ways in which governments, businesses, communities and individuals connect and share information, making them essential for everyday life.

This has meant the construction of vast networks of towers, transmitters and receivers to support mobile phone, broadband, television and radio services, and other data transmission requirements.

29

Test your knowledge

1 Which term describes all the systems and services that a country needs in order to function properly?

   a Superstructure

   b Constructure

   c Substructure

   d Infrastructure

2 Which type of building is a dormer bungalow?

   a Public

   b Domestic

   c Historic

   d Civic

3 What is the name for two dwellings joined together side by side?

   a Link-attached

   b Terraced

   c Semi-detached

   d Detached

4 What name is given to an architectural period of time distinguished by particular characteristics?

   a Era

   b Centenary

   c Stage

   d Generation

5 In which time period did public buildings start to be built with steel frames and a lot of concrete and glass in the design?

   a After the mid-seventeenth century

   b After the mid-eighteenth century

   c After the mid-nineteenth century

   d After the mid-twentieth century

6 Which category describes a building occupied by a company or business to make a trading profit?

   a Industrial

   b Commercial

   c Residential

   d Traditional

7 When serving the needs of a community, which category is a museum placed in?

a Social

b Cultural

c Traditional

d Conventional

8 What are A-roads also known as?

a Track roads

b Toll roads

c Trunk roads

d Trail roads

9 Which type of bridge uses cables attached to towers stretching across the full distance of the span?

a Truss

b Arched

c Suspension

d Cantilever

10 Which type of coastal defence is designed with a long sloping face to absorb the waves' energy?

a Gabion

b Revetment

c Groyne

d Sea wall

CHAPTER 2

INTRODUCTION TO THE TRADES IN THE CONSTRUCTION AND BUILT ENVIRONMENT SECTOR

INTRODUCTION

Every building or structure that forms part of the built environment is constructed by many trained, skilled and experienced workers co-operating to bring a development to successful completion. Trade specialists perform many different activities that are sometimes arranged in sequence and sometimes happen simultaneously over the course of a project.

This means that each trade specialist needs an understanding of the work roles of others, to ensure that work on site runs smoothly and with the minimum of disruption. In this chapter, we will discuss the work of different personnel in two key categories: those working in construction trades and those working as building services specialists.

LEARNING OUTCOMES

By the end of this chapter, you will:
1 know the trades in the construction and built environment sector
2 know the traditional skills used in construction and building services.

1 TRADES IN THE CONSTRUCTION AND BUILT ENVIRONMENT SECTOR

Whichever trade or specialism you choose to work in, you will need to understand how the skills and abilities you develop integrate with the activities of other skilled workers on site. Each worker can contribute to the smooth running of a construction project by considering how their work patterns and activities impact on others.

In this section, we will discuss two categories of work activities on site:

- construction work
- building services.

1.1 Construction work
Trowel occupations

The term 'trowel occupations' refers to operatives who produce masonry structures using brick, block or stone, working with mortar to assemble and fix the specified materials. The general titles bricklayer and stonemason are likely to be used when referring to skilled workers undertaking trowel occupations.

The range of work within this specialism includes:

- building walls that form structures or land boundaries in masonry
- constructing decorative features
- repairing damaged masonry.

Masonry work can be:

- above ground level for the visible sections of a structure
- below ground level for the foundations of a structure.

▼ Table 2.1 Main activities in trowel occupations

ACTIVITY

Search online for 'masonry footings'. Is this type of masonry constructed above ground or below ground?

Type of activity	Work description
Brickwork  ▲ A bricklayer at work on a housing site	Bricks are traditional materials that can be used to build the internal or external walls of a structure. Wall designs can vary in complexity, from those that use plain corners and straight lengths to those that include highly detailed features. A bricklayer's work could include new buildings or extensions, or perhaps **conservation and repair** work to existing buildings.
Blockwork  ▲ Foundations constructed in blockwork	Blocks are usually used in conjunction with bricks when constructing walls. However, some construction designs or elements such as masonry foundations might use only blocks for their construction. Because the face area of a single block equals the face area of six bricks, using blocks can significantly speed up the rate of production when building walls.
Stonework  ▲ A banker mason at work	There are two types of stonemason: banker masons and fixer masons. Banker masons are mainly based in workshops or stone-preparation areas on site. They cut and prepare stone from the quarry for use by fixer masons at the work location. The work involves carefully cutting and smoothing stone into shape using a range of hand and power tools.

KEY TERM

Conservation and repair: the process of bringing a building or structure back to its original state

▼ Table 2.1 Main activities in trowel occupations (continued)

Type of activity	Work description
 ▲ A fixer mason at work on a new building	Fixer masons assemble different types of stone in accordance with the design requirements of a building or other structure.

In time, bricklayers and stonemasons may have opportunities to develop their skills and experience in order to progress their career as a supervisor or manager. Many have succeeded in establishing their own businesses as **contractors** on large sites or working for private clients on individual developments such as new build or **renovation** projects. Bricklayers and stonemasons might also work in the conservation and repair of traditional and historic buildings.

Wood occupations

Workers in wood occupations are usually referred to as carpenters or joiners. They undertake a variety of skilled activities using timber, ranging from the production of structural building components to making carefully crafted furniture to be used within a building.

▼ Table 2.2 Main activities in wood occupations

Type of activity	Work description
Structural carcassing  ▲ A timber roof structure	The term 'carcassing' refers to assembled components of a structure made from timber, such as the roof or floor framework. Traditional roofs were called cut roofs, because individual lengths of timber were skilfully cut to size and shape by a carpenter on site. Modern roofs are more likely to be assembled by carpenters using **trussed rafters**. Carcassing can also refer to the frames of internal walls between the rooms of a building, called stud walls. (See 'First-fix carpentry' below.) Note: the framed structure of a built-in cupboard can also be called carcassing, but this is not structural.

▼ Table 2.2 Main activities in wood occupations (continued)

Type of activity	Work description
First-fix carpentry  ▲ A carpenter fixing a door lining	Broadly speaking, the term 'first fix' refers to the sequence of work completed before plastering commences. First-fix carpentry work includes: ● partition (stud) walls ● external door and window frames – if not installed when the walls are being built, they are fitted during first fix ● internal door lining – the initial component of the internal door frame ● stairs – fitted before the wall finishes start to be applied; the stairs will need temporary protection to avoid possible damage during subsequent construction operations.
Second-fix carpentry  ▲ Fitting kitchen units	Second-fix carpentry includes timber items that are classed as finishes, such as: ● skirting boards along the bottom of walls at floor level ● **architraves** surrounding door frames ● internal doors – these need to be protected from potential damage during subsequent operations such as applying paint finishes to walls and ceilings ● kitchen units – these also require temporary protection from damage by subsequent operations such as wall tiling.
Bespoke carpentry  ▲ Bespoke carpentry and joinery work	Bespoke carpentry and joinery work involves making customised timber items to fit individual requirements. This highly skilled work can include structural timber products such as purpose-made staircases or decorative feature items such as specialised window and door frames.

Carpenters and joiners can progress their careers in many ways.

● Those who have developed their skills and experience over time will be able to pursue supervisory and management roles.
● Those with organisational skills can become on-site contractors and employ others.
● Those who produce bespoke furniture can set up successful and lucrative businesses by dealing with clients who both appreciate and can afford the cost of high-quality work.

INDUSTRY TIP

Making bespoke furniture is sometimes referred to as 'cabinet making'

ACTIVITY

Bricklayers, carpenters and skilled workers in other trades can become contractors running their own businesses.

Discuss with a partner the advantages and disadvantages of being self-employed and running your own business. Make lists of your conclusions.

Plastering

A plasterer skilfully applies coats of finishing materials to:

- interior walls and ceilings, to produce surfaces suitable for the application of decorating materials
- external walls, to produce attractive weatherproof finishes.

▼ Table 2.3 Main activities in plastering

Type of activity	Work description
Internal plastering  ▲ Applying plaster to an internal wall	The internal area to be plastered must be carefully prepared to ensure that the plaster mix sticks to the backing material of the wall or ceiling. Plaster is usually applied in two coats, but more coats can be applied if a wall or ceiling is very uneven. Depending on the specification, internal masonry walls may first be coated with a sand and cement mix (render) to provide a solid flat surface over which **gypsum** plaster is applied to give a smooth finish. Depending on the air temperature and type of backing material, mixed plaster can set very quickly, so efficient planning and preparation and the ability to work quickly are essential.
External plastering  ▲ Applying external render	External walls can be coated with sand/cement render to give a suitable finish that resists the effects of bad weather. Typically, a 'scratch' coat is applied first, which literally has shallow scratches in it to allow further coats to bind firmly to it. Other types of render are available, using a range of modern materials that can offer different colours and textures.
Dry lining  ▲ Taping and filling the joints between plasterboards for dry lining	Dry lining is an increasingly common alternative to wet plastering. It reduces the amount of water used and can speed up the production process. The dry lining materials are usually plasterboard sheets fixed with screws to a stud framework. The screw holes are filled and sanded to a smooth finish. When fixing plasterboards to masonry walls, a special adhesive is used in a process sometimes referred to as 'dot and dab'. The gaps between the plasterboard sheets are covered with a special tape followed by a filler which is sanded to give an invisible join.

▼ Table 2.3 Main activities in plastering (continued)

Type of activity	Work description
Floor surfaces  ▲ Modern floor screeds can be pumped to the work location	Traditionally, plasterers applied a thin layer of sand and cement mix (a 'screed') to rough solid floors (such as concrete floors) to provide a smooth finish. More recently, if a floor screed is required, it will be installed by a specialist operative using a product designed to be pumped to the work location. Some types of pumped screed are self-levelling.
Fibrous plastering  ▲ Installing a moulded plaster ceiling rose	This method is often used to repair damaged plasterwork in older buildings. Adding fibrous material to the plaster mix means that: <ul><li>the finished product is stronger when set</li><li>it is easier to form complex decorative effects.</li></ul> Decorative plasterwork and panels can be produced using moulds, adding traditional fibrous materials such as horse hair or hessian, or modern alternatives such as glass fibres.

ACTIVITY

Research different types of render online. How many can you find? Write a description of a modern render and a historic render, including the materials they are manufactured from.

Plasterers can progress their careers in similar ways to bricklayers, stonemasons and carpenters.

- Those who have developed their skills and experience over time will be able to pursue supervisory and management roles.
- Many plasterers decide to become self-employed and set up their own businesses working as contractors or sub-contractors.
- Specialising in making decorative fibrous-plaster components for conservation and repair projects is a **heritage skill** that can be both interesting and rewarding.

ACTIVITY

Search online for images of decorative plaster mouldings. Select one that you like and make a sketch of it. Think about how skilled a worker needs to be to produce mouldings like these.

Decorative finishing and industrial painting occupations

Decorative finishes are applied to the interior and exterior of buildings by a skilled worker usually referred to as a painter and decorator. The work involves a thorough preparation stage to make sure that the finished job is attractive and long-lasting. On a construction project, attention to detail is especially important, since the work will be constantly on view to users of the building.

A painter and decorator could work in homes, offices, factories or even be involved in painting bridges or ships in an industrial setting using a range of access equipment.

▼ Table 2.4 Main activities in painting and decorating

Type of activity	Work description
Painting	Paint can be applied using brushes and rollers.
	Different types of paint are available depending on the finish required, such as emulsion, gloss or weather-resistant for exterior use.
	Applying a liquid material to achieve a uniform thickness on a surface requires practice in order to master the necessary methods, techniques and skills.
Decorating	The application of materials such as wallpaper and fabric to walls and ceilings is skilled work. Each piece of material must be accurately measured, cut and hung using the correct type of adhesive.
Special effects	A range of techniques can be used to create special effects. ● In 'rag rolling', a contrasting paint colour is applied over a base coat using roughly folded fabric to create random patterns. ● A wood effect can be created on a plain painted surface using special combs, using a technique called graining. ● The appearance of marble can be achieved by skilfully using special painting techniques to imitate the faults in the stone.
Spraying	Some types of paint or protective covering are applied using spray equipment. This method is particularly important where brush marks need to be avoided.

Career development for a painter and decorator could involve:

● moving into supervisory or management roles
● becoming self-employed and working as a contractor or sub-contractor
● specialising in particular aspects of the trade, such as interior design or the industrial sector (for example, applying advanced protective technical coatings to pipelines and storage tanks).

ACTIVITY

Use the internet to research spray painting and identify the different types of equipment used.

Roofing operations

Roofers install waterproof and windproof coverings on new and existing roofs using materials such as tile, slate, felt or sheet material. The work often involves measuring roofs and calculating the materials needed.

▼ Table 2.5 Main activities for roofing operatives

Type of activity	Work description
Flat-roof covering ▲ Flat roofing using built-up felt	A flat roof has a slope or incline of up to 10° (degrees) from horizontal. Flat roofs can be covered using: • sheet materials in plastic, steel or lightweight metals such as aluminium • built-up felt (multiple layers of mineral felt laid in hot bitumen) • mastic asphalt or GRP (glass-reinforced polymer/plastic) – liquid-applied systems used for waterproofing.
Pitched-roof covering ▲ Roofer working on a pitched roof	A pitched roof has a slope or incline greater than 10° (degrees) from horizontal. A roofer fixes a layer of protective felt over the timber roof framework. Precisely spaced timber battens are then fixed onto this, before attaching rows (or courses) of slates or tiles.

Career development for a roofer could involve:

• becoming self-employed and setting up their own business working as a contractor or sub-contractor
• focusing on applying and maintaining particular types of specialist roofing materials where market support exists, such as replacing defective felt roofs with GRP.

Construction and civil engineering

Civil-engineering operatives work on large building and infrastructure projects such as roads, bridges, tunnels, water-distribution systems, railways, airports and power stations. Work can be carried out in an office or on site, and typical activities can include:

• calculating materials and components
• establishing workforce requirements
• planning and keeping records of progress on site.

▼ Table 2.6 Main activities for civil-engineering operatives

Type of activity	Work description
Groundworks	Often, large quantities of soil must be moved to allow the correct positioning of buildings and other features on site. This process is generally referred to as groundworks. The term also applies to excavating trenches for drains and other services and preparing areas for the foundations of buildings.
Setting out	A vital first step for a construction project is the correct positioning or setting out on site of buildings, roads and services such as gas, electricity, water and drainage. The drawings showing the position of these elements can be difficult to interpret and understand.
	If elements were constructed in the wrong place and had to be moved, the costs would be significant. Therefore, a civil-engineering operative needs to be able to work carefully and accurately and must possess the skills to observe, analyse and problem-solve efficiently.
Paving	Paving roads and footpaths requires the creation of a solid and stable base to carry the intended traffic. This can mean shaping and contouring the ground to account for the intended route of the paving, so that gradients are not too steep and rainwater drains away adequately.
Drainage	Drainage systems are usually installed so that gravity provides the energy to transport waste (foul) and surface (storm) water to the intended destination for disposal. This means that the fall or incline of the drainage system must be designed carefully.
	Waste water must move in a controlled manner so that any solids are not left behind to obstruct the system. Sustainable drainage systems (SuDS) are vital to the efficient movement of waste and storm water, to prevent and control flooding without damage to the environment.
	(Later in this chapter, we will discuss the role of plumbers in installing drainage components.)

A civil-engineering operative can progress from working for a company to setting up their own business as an independent contractor. Their career path could potentially take them all over the world, working on challenging, exciting and iconic projects.

ACTIVITY

Search for 'the ten most impressive civil-engineering projects'. Select one of these projects and write a short report on why you found it interesting.

1.2 Building services
Electrotechnical work

Electricians install and maintain electrical services such as lighting and power in a wide range of buildings. They may work in houses, offices, factories and other domestic, commercial and industrial settings.

Electrical installation work is highly regulated and requires attention to detail and thoroughness to make sure that users of electrical appliances and equipment are kept safe. Correct installation also means that the building itself is protected from electrical fire hazards.

▼ Table 2.7 Main activities for electrotechnical workers

Type of activity	Work description
First-fix wiring 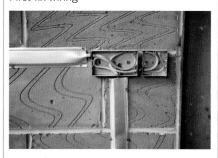 ▲ First-fix wiring is installed before plastering or dry lining	Remember, the term 'first fix' applies to items that are installed before plastering commences, so first-fix electrical work includes the installation of wiring and junctions that will not be visible when the building is completed. Cables for lighting are run through spaces above ceilings and power cables are fixed to walls, with metal capping protecting them from potential damage by subsequent plastering work. The position of switches and sockets is confirmed, with pattress boxes recessed into walls. If dry lining is specified rather than wet plastering, cables will be installed before the plasterboards are fixed in place.
Second-fix wiring  ▲ Second-fix wiring includes installing light switches	Once cables have been hidden beneath the wall finish, second-fix wiring involves making all the necessary connections to switches, sockets, distribution boards and meters. The visible items must be neatly installed, since this is part of the finished product. Testing the system is carried out when all connections are made and before external power is connected.

An electrician can advance their career by training as an electrical engineer. This type of work can involve the design and installation of complex systems, such as those used in telecommunications. Electrical engineers could be involved in the generation and supply of electricity, designing electrical industrial machinery or supervising the installation of heating, ventilation and lighting systems.

Plumbing

Plumbers install, maintain and repair:

- water and heating systems
- sanitary services
- pipework and controls for gas supplies.

Aspects of this work can be highly technical, requiring an understanding of mathematical calculations. Accuracy is important when calculating quantities such as the capacity of cylindrical water tanks or the required heat output from radiators for specific room sizes.

IMPROVE YOUR MATHS

Search online for 'plumbing calculations' and look through the images you find. Write down your impressions of how difficult they appear to be.

▼ Table 2.8 Main activities for plumbers

Type of activity	Work description
First and second fix of hot- and cold-water systems  ▲ First-fix plumbing	First-fix plumbing work involves installing pipework that will often be hidden after plastering or dry lining is complete. Separate pipework must be installed to carry hot and cold water and may be routed through ceiling and attic spaces. Careful planning is required to make sure that pipe runs are not longer than necessary when delivering hot and cold water efficiently to the point of use. Drainage pipes from sinks, showers and baths will also be installed as first-fix operations. Second-fix work includes: • installing water-storage tanks and cylinders • installing and connecting pipework for sinks, showers, baths and toilets.
Domestic heating systems  ▲ Domestic heating installation	A plumber installs pipework and **ducts** for heating systems, along with the control systems and appliances that produce the heat. Boilers for heating systems can run on gas, oil or electricity, and some plumbers specialise in installing and maintaining just one type (see 'Heating and ventilation' on page 43).
Surface- and waste-water drainage systems  ▲ New drainage system installation	Drainage systems for surface (storm) water and waste (foul) water must be installed in accordance with strict regulations. Efficient removal of surface and waste water must be done in a way that avoids pollution of the environment and prevents flooding. A plumber must carefully install pipework with the correct fall or angle of slope and must pressure-test the system to ensure that there are no leaks.

KEY TERM

Ducts: enclosed tubes, passages or channels for conveying liquid or gas

A trained, experienced plumber may choose to specialise in specific areas of work and start their own business working as a contractor.

Gas engineering

Gas engineers could work on:

- regional gas-transportation and gas-distribution systems
- the supply of gas to and the internal distribution of gas within buildings
- the monitoring of gas usage or fuel efficiency.

The work may require knowledge of gas burners, **plant** design, gas supply, **combustion** and manufacturing processes.

▼ Table 2.9 Main activities for gas engineers

Type of activity	Work description
Installation	Gas equipment and services must be installed in accordance with strict regulations. Incorrect installation could allow gas to leak into the environment or poisonous fumes to be given off – both highly dangerous situations. As a specialist, a gas installation engineer must: ● understand maths, science and technology ● be committed to keeping up to date with changes in regulations and advances in equipment design.
Servicing, repairs and maintenance	Gas installations must be regularly and meticulously maintained and serviced. Repairs to a system must be carried out promptly in accordance with regulations. Gas service engineers carry a high level of responsibility. They must be able to solve problems and use logical, analytical thinking.

Career development for a gas engineer may take the form of greater specialisation or, when suitably qualified and experienced, working as a **consultant**.

Heating and ventilation

Heating and ventilation engineers install, maintain and repair central-heating, ventilation and air-conditioning systems in industrial and commercial buildings. They must work accurately when installing equipment, in accordance with working drawings and **specifications**.

While there are some similarities with the work of a plumber, heating and ventilation engineers work on much larger-scale equipment.

KEY TERMS

Plant: machinery or equipment used for an industrial application

Combustion: the process of burning something, such as fuel

Consultant: an expert who provides advice professionally

Specification: a detailed description of the materials and working methods that must be used for a project

▲ Figure 2.1 Office heating and ventilation system

Heating systems in industrial and commercial buildings may use electricity, gas, oil or renewable energy sources such as wood pellets or air-/ground-source heat pumps.

The air-handling provisions for heating and ventilation systems include fans, ducts and flow-control equipment to efficiently channel warm air from the heat source to the building's occupants.

Similar systems are used to bring fresh air into the building and remove stale air for the comfort of the occupants. Air conditioning combines ventilation with cooling systems in order to maintain comfortable temperatures in hot weather.

Heating and ventilation engineers may decide to specialise in certain areas, for example:

- the air-conditioning aspect of ventilation systems requires technical skills in refrigeration, as well as an understanding of airflow through the delivery and extraction system
- some renewable heat sources, such as ground- or air-source heat pumps, are highly technical heat exchangers that require specialist installation and maintenance.

2 TRADITIONAL SKILLS USED IN CONSTRUCTION AND BUILDING SERVICES

Each area of construction and building services that we have discussed so far requires skills that have been refined and developed over a long time. We could define these as 'traditional' hand skills.

These skills can be divided into four categories:

- measuring/marking out
- cutting
- installing
- finishing.

These categories make it easier to understand how the skills are used by different trade workers on site, and how the activities of each worker might overlap.

2.1 The main traditional skills
Measuring/marking out

Most trades require the measuring and marking out of components or materials to ensure that work is completed in accordance with working drawings and specifications. Tables 2.10 and 2.11 show how this traditional skill is applied to different work activities.

▼ Table 2.10 How measuring is applied as a traditional skill in construction

| Trade | Forms of measuring | | |
	Linear measurement	Calculating area	Calculating volume
Bricklaying and stonemasonry	Measuring: • lengths and heights of walls • widths and heights of door and window openings • positions of internal walls • positions of openings for services below the ground	Calculating the area of the face of walls in m² (square metres) to work out the quantities of bricks/blocks/stone required	Calculating: • the volume of solid floors in m³ (cubic metres) to work out the quantities of concrete required • the volume of mortar required in m³
Carpentry and joinery	Measuring: • lengths of timber ready for cutting • lengths, widths and heights of structures to prepare assembled components to fit	Calculating the area of sheet material, such as plywood	Calculating the volume for bulk timber quantities
Plastering	Measuring: • lengths and heights of walls from corner to corner to establish **scrim tape** requirements • around reveals and heads of doors to establish **corner bead** requirements	Calculating the area of walls and ceilings to establish the quantity of plaster/plasterboard required	Calculating the volume of water required to mix plaster or wall adhesive
Painting and decorating	Measuring the lengths and heights of walls to calculate wallpaper/fabric requirements	Calculating the area of the face of walls in m² (square metres) to work out the quantity of paint/wall covering required	Calculating the volume of paint or other liquid materials required
Roofing	Measuring: • the lengths and widths of pitched roof surfaces to calculate the number of courses and correct overlap of slates/tiles • the lengths and widths of flat roof surfaces to calculate the quantity of felt/GRP rolls required	Calculating the area of roof surfaces to establish the number of sheets of covering material required	Calculating the volume of adhesives or other liquid materials required
Civil engineering	Measuring to establish: • site boundaries • accurate positions of structures, roads and services • slopes and gradients	Calculating the area of: • surfaces to establish drainage run-off requirements • site coverage, such as when installing water-control sheet or membrane materials	Calculating the volume of: • soil to be moved during groundworks or when digging excavations • materials for forming roads, pathways and paved areas

KEY TERMS

Linear measurement: the distance between two given points along a line

Area: the space occupied by a flat shape or the surface of an object

Volume: the total space in three dimensions taken up by an object, material or substance

Scrim tape: a strip of open-weave fabric used to strengthen joints between plasterboards

Corner bead: a strip of formed sheet metal placed on the outside corners of walls to protect the plastered edge

▼ Table 2.11 How measuring is applied as a traditional skill in building services

Trade	Forms of measuring		
	Linear measurement	Calculating area	Calculating volume
Electrical	Measuring cable runs to establish material requirements	Calculating wall/ceiling areas to establish heat-transfer rates	
Plumbing	Measuring pipework runs to establish material requirements	Calculating wall/ceiling areas to establish heat-transfer rates	Calculating: • room volumes to establish air-movement and heat-input requirements • the volume of water-storage tanks to meet requirements
Gas installation	Measuring pipework/ductwork runs to establish material requirements	Calculating wall/ceiling areas to establish heat-transfer rates	Calculating: • room volumes to establish air-movement and heat-input requirements • the volume of gas flow/flue gases
Heating and ventilation	Measuring pipework/ductwork runs to establish material requirements	Calculating wall/ceiling areas to establish heat-transfer rates	Calculating: • room volumes to establish air-movement and heat-input requirements • the volume of air flow/flue gases to and from heating boilers

Cutting

Most trades need to cut materials or components using hand tools or power tools. Tables 2.12 and 2.13 detail cutting operations where trades use hand tools.

▼ Table 2.12 How cutting by hand is applied as a traditional skill in construction

Trade	Forms of cutting by hand	
	Sheet materials	Components
Bricklaying and stonemasonry	Insulation sheet materials are cut using a saw or craft knife.	Bricks, blocks and stones are cut using a bolster chisel and club (or lump) hammer. Cutting and trimming can be done using a range of special types of hammer.
Carpentry and joinery	Sheet materials such as plywood are cut using a hand saw.	Timber components such as joists and rafters are cut using a hand saw. A range of special saws are used in joinery work to produce detailed items such as components for furniture.
Plastering	Plasterboard is cut using a hand saw or craft knife.	Scrim tape is cut to length using scissors, a craft knife or, more frequently, the sharp edge of a plastering trowel. Corner beads are cut to length using metal snips or a hacksaw.
Painting and decorating	Wallpaper and fabric wall coverings are cut using decorators' scissors or a craft knife.	
Roofing	Slates are cut using specialist cutters or saws. Sheet materials for flat roofs, such as plywood, are cut using a hand saw. Metal, plastic and GRP sheets are cut using specialist saws.	Many metal components used in roofing activities are cut using a hacksaw. Note: some roofing materials, such as clay ridge tiles, can only be cut using power tools.

▼ Table 2.13 How cutting by hand is applied as a traditional skill in building services

Trade	Forms of cutting by hand	
	Sheet materials	Components
Electrical		Cables are cut using specialist cutters or snips. Cable **trunking** or sheathing can be cut using snips or a hacksaw.
Plumbing	Sheet materials, such as lead for weatherproofing purposes, can be cut using specialist knives and snips.	Pipes are cut using specialist cutters.
Gas installation		Pipes are cut using specialist cutters.
Heating and ventilation	Sheet metal for small-scale fabrication of ducts and metal boxes for air-handling units can be cut using metal saws.	Cables are cut using specialist cutters or snips. Cable trunking or sheathing can be cut using snips or a hacksaw. Pipes and hoses are cut using specialist tools.

Installing

Installation skills can be applied to a wide range of materials, components and equipment for each trade.

As well as installing items as part of a new structure, it may be necessary to install materials or components during repair or renovation of a structure. Each situation will require slightly different skills.

Trowel occupations

When installing brick, block and stone, workers in trowel occupations will use hand skills to prepare and manipulate a mortar mix. The consistency and strength of the mix will depend on the characteristics of the material being installed and the type of work being undertaken.

The skills and level of ability required for the work task will vary according to the circumstances.

Plasterers

The material being applied and the backing material will determine how the installation work is planned and undertaken.

Drying and **curing** times of the plaster will vary, depending on the:

- type of material being applied
- absorbency of the backing material
- air temperature and **humidity** at the work location.

A plasterer may also install sheet materials, fixing heavy plasterboards to walls and ceilings using screw fixings or special adhesives. Purpose-built lifting and positioning equipment has been developed to make fixing boards to ceilings easier and safer.

ACTIVITY

Search online for 'construction hand cutting tools'.

In a Microsoft Word document, for each of the trades listed in Tables 2.12 and 2.13:

- copy and paste an image of an appropriate hand cutting tool
- label the image and write a short description of the tool.

HEALTH AND SAFETY

All cutting operations have the potential to cause injury to the user and others nearby. Every work activity and work situation on site will be assessed to establish the hazards and potential hazards that can arise. This is done by carrying out a risk assessment, which determines ways of reducing, managing or removing risks. There is more on this in Chapter 5.

KEY TERMS

Trunking: a cover used to hide and protect electrical wires in a building

Curing: the process of a material becoming hard by cooling, drying or crystallisation

Humidity: a measurement of the amount of water vapour or 'wetness' in the air

▲ Figure 2.2 Installing plasterboards

Carpenters and joiners

Carpenters and joiners carry out installation work at many different locations in a structure. A range of skills are needed to install floors, roofs and internal walls.

Many modern buildings use a timber frame rather than traditional masonry as their structural core. This means that a carpenter might be responsible for a large part of the overall installation work, including:

- structural elements of the building
- internal fittings, such as doors, door linings, window sills, skirtings and architraves
- functional items, such as kitchen units and cupboards.

▲ Figure 2.3 A timber-frame structure

Electrical and plumbing

As mentioned previously, electrical and plumbing installation work is split into two stages, described as first and second fix.

- First-fix installation is not visible after plastering or dry lining is complete. Since cables and pipes installed during first fix will most likely be inaccessible in the completed building, it is vital that all connections and joints are made carefully and correctly. For example, faulty pipework installation can lead to water leaks, which can cause extensive damage and be expensive to repair.
- Second-fix installation must also be carried out with care. Electrical switches, sockets and other fittings must be installed with the correct internal connections and positioned accurately to provide a neat appearance. Plumbing components such as sanitary ware are expensive and can be easily damaged during installation.

Finishing

The finish is the appearance of completed work. Providing a high-quality finish should be the aim of skilled workers who take pride in their work.

To achieve high standards, operatives must pay attention to detail and assess where changes can be made to improve quality.

'Wet' trades mostly use liquid-based materials, which can be difficult to apply and manipulate. They require a high level of skill to produce a consistently high-quality finish, as outlined in Table 2.14.

▼ Table 2.14 Skills required when finishing

Trade	Skills required when finishing
Bricklaying and stonemasonry  ▲ Jointing to produce a finish to brickwork	The quality of finish in brickwork, blockwork and stonework depends on how well the materials have been laid. Uniformity and accuracy are vital to achieving a high-quality finish. The mortar joints in masonry work are usually 'jointed' to produce a finish. This involves using special tools to create a smooth joint to the specified profile. Sometimes, the specified finish requires the mortar joints to be raked (or scraped) out to a given depth before a different mortar mix (perhaps a different colour or consistency) is 'pointed' into the joints.
Plastering  ▲ Plaster gives a smooth finish	Mixing plaster to the correct consistency is the first step in producing a high-quality finish. Plastering should produce a finish to a wall or ceiling that is smooth, flat and consistent in absorbency. This is achieved by trowelling the surface of the applied plaster at the right time during the drying and curing process. Judging the right time to work on the wet surface takes skill and experience and the application of unique hand skills and techniques. If dry lining is specified, plasterboards must be carefully installed to achieve a uniform flat surface. If the boards are fixed to a stud wall, this is relatively easy to achieve. If the boards are fixed to a masonry wall using special adhesive, it is much harder to align them accurately along the length of the wall. A high-quality finish relies on the skill and care employed when filling and smoothing the joints between boards.

▼ Table 2.14 Skills required when finishing (continued)

Trade	Skills required when finishing
Plastering (continued)	The wall and ceiling finish achieved by the plasterer will directly impact on the quality of the work produced by follow-on trades such as painters/decorators and tilers. Plasterers may also produce floor finishes in the form of screeds. These must be smooth, level and uniform in consistency.
Painting and decorating ▲ Applying a finishing coat of paint to a masonry feature	Though some may not class painting and decorating as a 'wet' trade, it does extensively use liquid products that require specific skills to achieve a high-quality finish. The quality of the final result greatly depends on the preparation stage. Paint will not hide or fill dips or hollows in a surface. These must be carefully filled with the right material and smoothed prior to painting. Timber items must be carefully prepared, with treatments applied to ensure that the wood is stable and the applied finish is durable. Painting is carried out in stages by applying a number of coats of different types of paint to achieve the specified finish. To apply paint to a vertical surface such as a wall or door requires a high degree of skill and practised technique, along with the selection of correct tools. The paint must be applied to the surface to achieve a uniform thickness, without it running down to produce streaks or irregularities. Decorating a wall or ceiling with paper or fabric also requires skill and practice to achieve a high-quality finish. Careful trimming where wall and ceiling surfaces meet is essential to achieving a neat and attractive appearance. Selecting the correct adhesive and relevant preparation treatments depends on experience, as well as the ability to interpret written instructions provided for specific projects.

2.2 Appropriate materials used for traditional and historic buildings

In Chapter 1, we discussed some traditional building designs and structures in Wales. There are many buildings and structures of historic significance, which require frequent maintenance and repair.

Since construction working practices and the types of materials used have changed significantly over time, it is essential that work on older buildings and structures uses only methods and materials that are suitable.

For example, most traditional buildings are made of vapour-permeable materials that do not incorporate barriers to external moisture. This creates a 'breathable' form of construction that tends to allow moisture to be absorbed and harmlessly released by evaporation. The use of vapour barriers and other impermeable materials commonly found in modern buildings, such as cement and gypsum plaster, should therefore be avoided when undertaking repairs or making alterations to traditional buildings. These materials can trap and hold moisture, hasten decay and reduce the temperature of walls, thereby encouraging condensation and mould growth.

ACTIVITY

Are there any historic buildings near where you live? Take some photographs of buildings in your area that you think are traditional designs or of historical significance. Discuss the buildings with others in your learner group to determine when they were constructed.

Lime plasters and renders

While modern wall finishes are often created using gypsum plaster and sand/cement render, traditional wall finishes in historic structures comprised plaster, render and putty produced using lime.

Lime is made from heated limestone, which is crushed to form a powder that can be used in a mortar mix for plastering or rendering. It is known for its ability to let structures 'breathe', helping to reduce internal damp problems.

▲ Figure 2.4 Renewing lime plaster at Salisbury Cathedral

Timber lath backgrounds

The use of plasterboards to create a flat surface when producing internal walls and ceilings in modern buildings is relatively fast and efficient. Previously, a more time-consuming method called 'timber lathing' was used to create a base for plastering.

This consisted of thin strips of timber ('laths') attached to a timber framework, over which lime plaster was applied. The laths were fixed to the timber frame with gaps between them that allowed the plaster to squeeze through slightly, keeping the surface in position when hardened.

ACTIVITY

Find out about the use of lime in plastering by searching online for 'lath and plaster'. When would it be more appropriate to use lath and plaster than gypsum plaster on plasterboards? Write a short report.

Timber

In the past, construction made extensive use of large, heavy timber components to make structures strong and long-lasting. Modern buildings increasingly use engineered timber components; this allows the use of smaller sized timbers, making components lighter and easier to install without compromising on strength.

▲ Figure 2.5 Historic timber-framed building, Powys, Wales

Other traditional materials

Traditional materials like slate and stone were used extensively in buildings throughout Wales and were often sourced from local quarries.

Sheet metals, such as copper and lead, were used to make roofs and vulnerable parts of buildings resistant to the effects of bad weather.

Ongoing repair and maintenance of historic buildings is creating demand for the heritage skills needed when working with these materials.

Test your knowledge

1 Why is it important for skilled workers to know about the work practices of other trades?

   a To make sure they have the best work location on site

   b To have a better chance of being promoted to supervisor

   c To be able to tell other workers how to do their job

   d To contribute to the smooth running of the project

2 Which term refers to the process of bringing a building or structure back to its original state?

   a Renovation

   b Rebuilding

   c Conservation and repair

   d Reclamation

3 Which term describes a person or company that agrees legal terms to provide a paid service?

   a Director

   b Contractor

   c Spokesperson

   d Administrator

4 Which skilled worker would install 'structural carcassing'?

   a Plasterer

   b Electrician

   c Carpenter

   d Engineer

5 To which trades do the terms 'first and second fix' apply?

   a Bricklaying, block laying and stonemasonry

   b Electrical, plumbing and carpentry

   c Civil engineering, heating and ventilation

   d Plastering, roofing and painting

6 Which skilled operative would undertake 'setting out' on a project site?

   a Electrical engineer

   b Carpenter

   c Civil engineer

   d Roofer

7 Which of the following trades falls under 'building services'?

   a Plumbing

   b Bricklaying

   c Carpentry

   d Plastering

8 Which term describes an expert who provides advice professionally?

a Authority

b Consultant

c Supervisor

d Manager

9 What does the term 'finishing' mean for a bricklayer?

a The brickwork activity on site is now fully completed

b The surplus bricks and blocks have been removed

c The bricks allocated to the job have been used up

d The brickwork has been jointed or pointed properly

10 What is an advantage of using lime plaster rather than gypsum plaster when working on historic buildings?

a It is known for its ability to let structures 'breathe', which helps to reduce damp

b It is not affected by humidity or air temperature at the work location

c It hardens quickly during application when the air temperature is low

d It is easier to mix large quantities to cover greater areas of wall or ceiling

Guided discussion

1 Explain the benefits of understanding the roles of other workers on site.

2 Describe the differences in the skills and activities of construction workers and building services workers.

3 Why can hand skills be described as 'traditional'?

4 What are 'wet' trades and why do they require high skill levels to produce an acceptable finish?

5 If you were given a work task on a historic building, why would it be better to use the same materials that were used when the building was constructed (if they are available)?

CHAPTER 3

INTRODUCTION TO THE BUILT ENVIRONMENT LIFE CYCLE

INTRODUCTION

Careful thought and skilful planning are required to create and maintain the built environment. In this chapter, we will discuss how planning decisions and systems of work are defined and applied to create safe and efficient buildings and structures. They must be designed to minimise damage to the natural environment, from the planning stage right through to the end of their useful life.

Buildings and other structures require significant physical resources throughout their life cycle, and planners must consider the potential effects on the environment of maintenance and conservation activities. We will consider how reusing existing buildings and recycling materials from demolished buildings are important aspects of supporting a sustainable built environment.

LEARNING OUTCOMES

By the end of this chapter, you will:
1 understand the design of buildings and structures
2 know the planning process
3 understand the stages of construction and the installation of services
4 know the methods of promoting services offered within the construction and built environment sector
5 know the types and purposes of maintenance of buildings, structures and installed services
6 understand repurposing of buildings and structures
7 know the process for demolition and destruction of buildings and structures.

1 THE DESIGN OF BUILDINGS AND STRUCTURES

Building safe and durable structures that work efficiently is a complex process that requires the application of a range of skills and construction principles. In this section, we will look at the way a project is organised to support sustainability by carefully working to plans and managing waste throughout the construction process.

1.1 Surveying

Surveyors are trained to take exact measurements and determine property boundaries. Their role includes calculating heights, depths, relative positions, property lines and other characteristics of terrain. Some ways in which their skills are applied on site are detailed in Table 3.1.

▼ Table 3.1 Different surveying activities

Activity	Purpose
Set out levels	• Establish heights and depths of roads in relation to the surrounding landscape • Set out depths of drains below ground and establish levels between locations along pipework to create a specified **fall** • Establish specified depths of foundations
Calculate area and volume	• Calculate surface area of ground (for example, calculate surface water run-off to establish drainage requirements) • Calculate volume of soil and other loose materials (spoil) to be moved on site or removed from site
Determine positions	• Establish location of buildings on site in relation to boundaries and other fixed reference points • Establish and confirm location of infrastructure elements, such as roads, bridges and tunnels
Calculate spacings and angles	• Calculate and set out spacings between adjacent buildings • Set out angles of buildings in relation to each other and site features such as roads and footpaths

KEY TERMS

Fall: the specified angle of slope between two points

Datum: a fixed point or height from which reference levels can be taken

Surveying principles

A surveyor uses established methods and principles to make exact calculations and set out measured positions accurately.

To establish heights and depths on site, a reference point called a **datum** is set up. This is referred to as a temporary bench mark (TBM). The TBM often takes the form of a peg, which is secured in concrete and protected from potential disturbance by machinery movements or other construction activities. It is important that the TBM is not disturbed, since all levels for buildings and structures on a site are transferred from it.

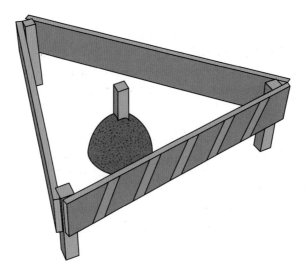

INDUSTRY TIP

Sometimes, a fixed point, such as an inspection-chamber cover in a road near to the site, may be used as a datum.

▲ Figure 3.1 Datum point (TBM) protected from disturbance

The TBM is taken from a permanent reference point, known as an ordnance bench mark (OBM). In the United Kingdom, OBMs are survey reference points made by a regulated organisation called Ordnance Survey. Most commonly, they are found on old buildings or other long-standing features.

▲ Figure 3.2 Ordnance bench mark

Although the physical network of OBMs is no longer being updated, this feature is still in existence in many places, and the markers will remain until they are eventually destroyed by redevelopment or erosion. The location of OBMs around the country can now be conveniently referenced through a licensed database.

ACTIVITY

Visit www.ordnancesurvey.co.uk/benchmarks and find out what ODN stands for.

For surveying small, flat areas of land to establish linear measurements, a method known as chain surveying can be used. This method uses a specially designed chain equipped with handles at either end for use by two operatives. A variety of lengths are available, from 5 metres up to 30 metres, with marks at every metre along the length of the chain.

This is not a highly accurate method of surveying and is only suitable for ground that is level, without obstructions or **undulations**. For larger land spaces, where there are many obstacles such as trees or existing buildings, a method known as compass surveying can be used. This uses a magnetic instrument to measure horizontal angles along a line of sight which are combined with linear measurements to establish specific points on the land. (See the description of 'compass' in Table 3.2.)

KEY TERM

Undulation: a wavy form or outline

KEY TERM

Invert level: the bottom of the inside of a drainage pipe within an inspection chamber

Equipment for surveying

Surveying equipment often uses sophisticated systems and requires training before use. Table 3.2 outlines the characteristics of different types of surveying equipment and how they are used.

▼ Table 3.2 Surveying equipment

Type	Characteristics	Uses
Theodolite	● Measures horizontal and vertical angles ● Tripod-mounted ● Optical sight lens for visual reference	● To establish precise positional points on site ● To measure heights of buildings using mathematics (triangulation) ● Extensively used in civil engineering, for example, to plot routes and elevations of highways
Automatic optical level	● Optical, tripod-mounted ● Used in conjunction with a graduated staff, requiring two-person operation ● Once set up and levelled, maintains level automatically when rotated	● To transfer levels from a TBM ● To check levels of corner points of buildings during foundation construction ● To check specified falls for drains ● To set cover and **invert levels** for inspection chambers
Laser level	● Often self-levelling, tripod-mounted ● One-person operation – once it is set up in a convenient location, the operator can move around site with a staff-mounted receiver to check levels	● Used for the same purposes as automatic optical level
Scanner	● Usually tripod-mounted ● Uses laser technology to capture large volumes of 3D data ● Also captures a photographic record of the subject being surveyed	● To capture data to create 3D imagery ● To support Building Information Modelling (see Chapter 6) ● Ideal for remote use in hazardous situations

▼ Table 3.2 Surveying equipment (continued)

Type	Characteristics	Uses
Compass	• Small instrument consisting of a magnetic needle, a graduated circle and a line-of-sight viewer • Relies on the magnetic field of the Earth's core to operate; accurate readings can be disturbed by electricity power lines or large iron structures nearby • A gyroscopic compass uses the physical forces generated by a fast-spinning heavy wheel to maintain a reference position	• To carry out compass surveying (see page 57)

ACTIVITY

Search online to find out what a laser level costs. Make a note of the cheapest and the most expensive models you can find. Why do you think there is such a wide range of prices?

1.2 The environmental impact of construction

When land is used for construction, there is less land available for agricultural and recreational purposes, resulting in permanent changes to the landscape. When designing and planning a construction project, the impact on nature, wildlife and the wider human community must be carefully considered.

The materials used for construction often have high levels of what is referred to as **embodied energy**. This is the total energy consumed during:

- extraction of raw materials
- manufacture of components
- transport of raw materials and components to the point of use
- application or installation of materials and components.

ACTIVITY

Research how much carbon is produced when manufacturing concrete. If a construction project like the Principality Stadium in Cardiff used thousands of tons of concrete, think about the impact on the environment.

A construction project also increases the amount of traffic within and around a site. This can result in pollution, dust and fumes, all of which will negatively impact the local community, possibly over an extended period of time.

INDUSTRY TIPS

You may hear a theodolite referred to as a 'total station theodolite' on site.

Intricate surveying equipment can be affected by vibration and moisture. Make sure the equipment is returned to its protective carrying case and stored in a dry place, preferably with an even, constant temperature.

KEY TERM

Embodied energy: the total energy required by all the activities associated with a production process. The carbon this process produces is sometimes referred to as 'embodied carbon' or 'capital carbon'

Construction and maintenance of the built environment can therefore have a potentially significant impact on the natural environment, and everyone involved in the sector should consider ways in which they can contribute to reducing this impact.

Table 3.3 looks at some of the factors that must be considered to minimise the environmental impact of construction activities.

▼ Table 3.3 Minimising the environmental impact of construction activities

Factor	Potential impact	Minimising the impact
Land use	Increased pressure on transport networks and infrastructure	Schedule combined and bulk deliveries to site to reduce delivery frequency
		Promote the use of public transport for on-site personnel travelling to and from work
	Natural drainage interruption	Maintain and preserve natural water courses as part of the design brief
	Increased flooding risk	Use **attenuation ponds** as part of on-site drainage systems
	Extraction of minerals for building materials scarring the landscape and destroying habitats	Sensitively reinstate mineral-extraction excavations
Pollution	Contamination of: ● air ● land ● water sources	Implement and maintain strict pollution-control measures Train and educate construction personnel to support a culture of pollution prevention
Hazardous substances	Negative effects on: ● human health ● wildlife ● agriculture	Strictly implement COSHH Regulations (see Chapter 5)
Waste	Energy required to transport waste during disposal	Accurately calculate quantities of materials and components required
	Energy required to process waste	Ensure good housekeeping and careful storage of materials on site
	Energy required to recycle waste	Create a culture of awareness of the consequences of unnecessary waste **Segregate** waste ready for recycling

To encourage efforts to reduce the environmental impact of pollution, a principle known as 'polluter pays' has evolved, under which those who produce pollution should bear the costs of managing it. The potential damage to human health or the environment through construction activities is brought into clear focus when the possibility of a financial penalty is applied.

IMPROVE YOUR ENGLISH

Research 'polluter pays UK' online. Write a short report on how the principle is applied and the sort of activities it applies to.

1.3 Sustainability

Homes, places of work and all the other elements of the built environment that serve the needs of society must be planned and constructed so as not to damage the environmental needs of future generations. By careful and intelligent planning, buildings and structures can be integrated into their surrounding environment to blend with it sustainably.

▲ Figure 3.3 A building blending with its surroundings

Constructing and operating a building uses significant amounts of energy, often referred to as a 'carbon footprint'. This is because producing energy by burning **fossil fuels** introduces carbon into the atmosphere. This combines with oxygen to form carbon dioxide, a gas which many scientists believe is causing **climate change**. Fossil fuels are not sustainable. They have taken millions of years to form, so they will not be quickly replaced and they have limited availability.

Construction projects must make greater use of renewable energy sources that are sustainable, such as solar and wind, in both:

- the manufacture of construction materials and components
- the way that buildings are designed to operate.

The amount of energy used to heat and cool buildings can be reduced by efficient insulation and ventilation management. This can be specified at the design stage.

ACTIVITY

Find out how air-source heat pumps work. Would you say these machines contribute to sustainability? Make a list of the advantages and disadvantages of using them and discuss your conclusions with someone else in your learner group.

KEY TERMS

Fossil fuels: natural fuels such as coal, oil and gas, formed from the ancient remains of living organisms

Climate change: a large-scale, long-term change in our planet's weather patterns and average temperatures

In order to support sustainability and protect the environment, it is also important to choose materials that have the lowest carbon footprint possible. Consider the following questions.

- **How far have the materials been transported?**
  Materials from a nearby source will reduce the amount of carbon generated during transport. Think about the carbon footprint of slates sourced in Wales compared with slates transported from China or India.
- **Does the source of the materials support sustainability?**
  For example, timber for construction should be obtained from managed forests, where trees are replanted after harvesting to maintain a sustainable source of timber for the future.
- **Is the manufacturing process designed to minimise waste?**
  Many construction materials such as brick, glass, timber and concrete can be recycled or reused. Waste management is important to support reuse and recycling at the point of manufacture and on site.

The land on which a building is constructed is no longer available for vegetation or as a habitat for wildlife. To reduce the effects of land loss, a sustainable practice that is being increasingly used is to install a 'green roof', sometimes referred to as a 'living roof'. This is formed by installing additional waterproof membranes and drainage mediums, onto which soil is added to allow growth of vegetation. This creates an **ecosystem** that maintains **biodiversity**.

This attractive, sustainable roof system restores wildlife habitat lost beneath the building's footprint, provides added insulation and absorbs rainwater in the vegetation growth. Up to 75 per cent of rainwater falling on a green roof can be retained, which is then gradually released back into the atmosphere, reducing the reliance on storm-water drainage systems.

ACTIVITY

Search online for images of green roofs in the UK. Copy and paste three images into a Microsoft Word document and state why you chose these examples.

To conserve water, rainwater from roof surfaces can also be used in 'grey water' systems to flush toilets. New structures may be designed to include drainage systems that store rainwater in tanks, which are frequently buried underground to allow heavy high-capacity tanks to be used. This is often referred to as 'water harvesting' and an example is shown in Figure 3.4. Water use by the occupants of a building should be managed by installing appliances that limit water consumption wherever possible.

To support sustainability, design of a new building should consider the following points.

- Conserve ecosystems and biodiversity by protecting existing natural resources such as trees and shrubs and integrating them into the project design. Avoid unnecessary disturbance of soil during construction.

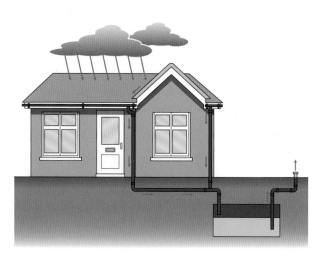

▲ Figure 3.4 Rainwater stored in an underground tank

- Wherever possible, optimise land use by utilising 'brownfield' sites (land that has been previously used for dwellings or industry), because this reduces the need to utilise 'greenfield' sites (land that has never been used for construction).
- Diligently reduce energy consumption during the construction phase. Carefully select materials and components that minimise energy consumption during manufacture. Source materials locally to reduce energy used in transport.
- Incorporate energy-conservation features throughout the building design. Install renewable energy systems for heating, cooling and ventilation.
- Design buildings and structures with adaptable spaces to optimise their use. Utilise building components that can be disassembled and repositioned for flexibility.
- Design buildings and structures to use local resources. Eliminate the use of toxic or hazardous materials as much as possible. Utilise recycled, reused and repurposed materials and components. The present generation's waste can become the next generation's raw materials.

1.4 Designing waste out of projects

Standardisation

Careful design can contribute to the reduction of waste by incorporating standardised sizes of components and materials. Standardised products have been used in construction for decades. For example, bricks and blocks are manufactured to standard sizes, allowing faster construction times compared with the use of materials of non-standard shape or size such as natural stone.

Designing the length of walls to correspond with standardised brick lengths makes the cutting of bricks unnecessary, reducing waste. This principle can be applied to many materials, resulting in significant reductions in waste in the construction phase of a building.

IMPROVE YOUR MATHS

If a standard roof tile is 420 mm wide, how many would be needed in one row (or course) for a roof 14.7 metres wide?

Storage

Storing materials in a considered way can also reduce waste. An example is the storage of cement on site. If new stock delivered to site is simply piled on top of existing stock, the older material will be left in storage for longer than it should be, leading to deterioration and waste. The storage arrangement should allow for existing stock to be used before newer stock. This process is called stock rotation.

▲ Figure 3.5 Cement bags carefully stored

At the design stage, it is possible to identify critical points for delivery of items which may be subject to deterioration, and a plan can be created to allow phased delivery to site.

Monitoring of materials susceptible to damage or deterioration should continue on site throughout construction activities, to reduce unnecessary waste. Sustainable materials sourced locally should be utilised as much as possible and stored carefully.

Recycling, reusing and repurposing

Recycling can be supported by the segregation of different types of waste for easier processing. For example, offcuts of timber can be used for producing new resources such as timber sheet materials for floor construction. Brick and block waste from cutting operations can be crushed and used as **aggregate** in some types of concrete.

Recycling results in less new material being extracted from the ground and less potentially damaging material ending up in landfill. Because of these benefits, it has been termed a 'virtuous circle', which can result in significant reductions in carbon emissions if managed and implemented well.

ACTIVITY

Search online for 'Wales recycling rates' and find out how well the Welsh Government is supporting recycling.

Reusing complete items from previous applications is also a method of reducing waste and protecting the environment. An important factor in selecting items and components for reuse is assessment of performance. Previously used materials and components must comply with current building regulations to be suitable for use in a new building. For this reason, they are often used for decorative applications rather than structural elements.

Repurposing and reusing materials and components provides the opportunity for novel design approaches in creating interesting and unusual structures, which enhance the attractiveness of the built environment.

1.5 Plans and documents used in construction

Plans and drawings are documents required at every stage of building work. They are an efficient way of providing a great deal of clear information, without the need for lots of potentially confusing text.

When producing drawings, an architectural technician or a draughtsperson will draw a building to **scale**. This means that a large structure is represented with accurate proportions on a document that is much smaller, which is more manageable than if it were drawn full size. Imagine trying to produce a drawing of a football stadium to its actual size – it would be impossible to work with.

Scale is shown using a **ratio**, such as 1 to 10. This would usually be written in the form '1:10' and means that if we wanted to draw a component that is 1 m (or 1000 mm) long, it would be shown as a drawing 100 mm long. This is because 100 mm is one-tenth of 1000 mm.

IMPROVE YOUR MATHS

On A4 paper (in landscape), use a ruler to draw a rectangular building to a scale of 1:10. The building must be 2.5 m long and 1.5 m wide.

Types of plans and drawings

There are a range of drawings, presented in different scales, that communicate distinct details to a skilled operative. Table 3.4 shows the different types of drawings, their purpose and the scales they are presented in.

▼ Table 3.4 Types of plans and drawings

Type of drawing	Description
Block plan Green St / Sand St / Plot 1 / Plot 2 / Plot 3	This is categorised as a 'location drawing'. It shows the proposed development in relation to surrounding properties. It must be based on an up-to-date map and drawn at an identified scale (typically 1:1250 or 1:2500). It usually shows individual plots and road layouts on the site as a simple outline with few dimensions.

⇒

▼ Table 3.4 Types of plans and drawings (continued)

Type of drawing	Description
Site plan	This is also categorised as a 'location drawing'. It shows the proposed development in relation to the property boundary (usual scale is 1:200 or 1:500). It also shows the positions of drainage and other services as well as access roads and drives. It may show the position of trees and shrubs if they are part of the planning requirements. (There is more information on planning permission and planning processes later in this chapter.)
Detail drawing	This type of drawing shows accurate, large-scale details of the construction of a particular item; it is most commonly used for carpentry and joinery items. (Usual scales are 1:2 and 1:5.) An example would be a setting out rod. This is not actually a rod but usually a thin piece of sheet material such as plywood, on which is drawn a full-size representation of the item to be made.
Assembly drawing	This is used to show how components fit together at specific locations. It is drawn to scales of 1:5, 1:10 and 1:20.
Range drawing	This provides information for manufacturers producing various components, such as purpose-made doors, windows or kitchen units. A range drawing could also show a manufacturer's standard range of items available 'off the shelf'. (Usual scales are 1:10 and 1:20.)

KEY TERMS

Conventions: agreed, consistent standards and rules

Elevation: a view of the front, back or sides of a building

Plan view: a view from above a building; a 'bird's eye' view

Plans and drawings are produced using **conventions**. This means that the format and layout of drawings follow agreed standards, allowing the information they contain to be consistently understood. When drawings are produced, they can be set out in a number of ways.

Presentation of plans and drawings

Two common methods of presenting drawings are:

- orthographic projection
- isometric projection.

Orthographic projection

Orthographic projection is a two-dimensional method of laying out a drawing, where the front **elevation** of a structure has the **plan view** directly below it. The side or end elevations are shown directly each side of the front elevation.

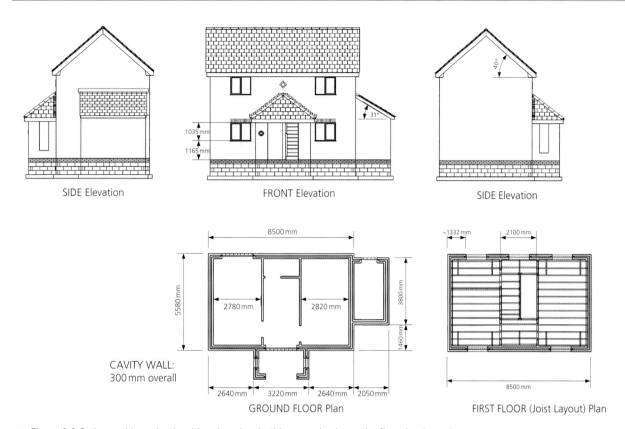

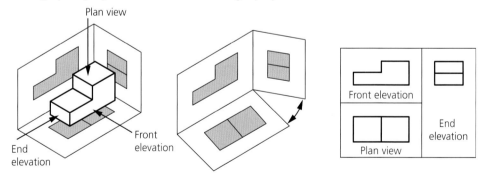

▲ Figure 3.6 Orthographic projection (the plan view in this example shows the floorplan layout)

This method of drawing allows views of all elevations to be looked at in relation to each other, in order to understand the overall layout of the structure. It makes it easy to see the measurements of a building, the position of doors and windows, the shape of the roof structure and much more. The most commonly used type of orthographic projection is called 'first-angle projection'.

▲ Figure 3.7 First-angle orthographic projection

Isometric projection

Isometric projection is a pictorial method of presenting information on a drawing. The structure is drawn at specified angles, with one corner represented as closer to the person viewing the drawing.

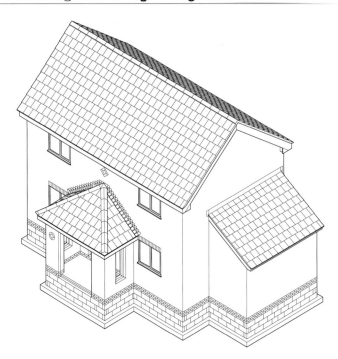

▲ Figure 3.8 An isometric projection drawing

This type of drawing can add greater clarity, giving the viewer a more lifelike representation of the building. Although it does not provide a true three-dimensional view (since it does not include **perspective**), it presents a more realistic view while maintaining accurate scaled dimensions on the drawing.

In isometric projection:

- the vertical lines of the structure or object will be drawn at 90° to the horizontal (or bottom edge of the page)
- the horizontal lines of the structure or object will be drawn at 30° to the horizontal.

Wiring diagrams

A wiring diagram is a simplified visual representation of the layout of an electrical system or circuit. It shows how electrical wires are interconnected and where fixtures such as switches, sockets and lighting components are positioned.

Symbols used on plans and drawings

Standardised symbols are used on drawings as a means of giving information in a simpler way. Labelling a drawing with all the individual parts of a building, such as a toilet or sink unit, would soon make it crowded with text, which could potentially be confusing.

Materials can be represented on a drawing using hatchings – a standardised set of lines and symbols. It is important that these conform to a standard, so that everyone using the drawing can interpret the information consistently and accurately. Study Figure 3.9 to see what symbols and hatchings on a construction drawing mean.

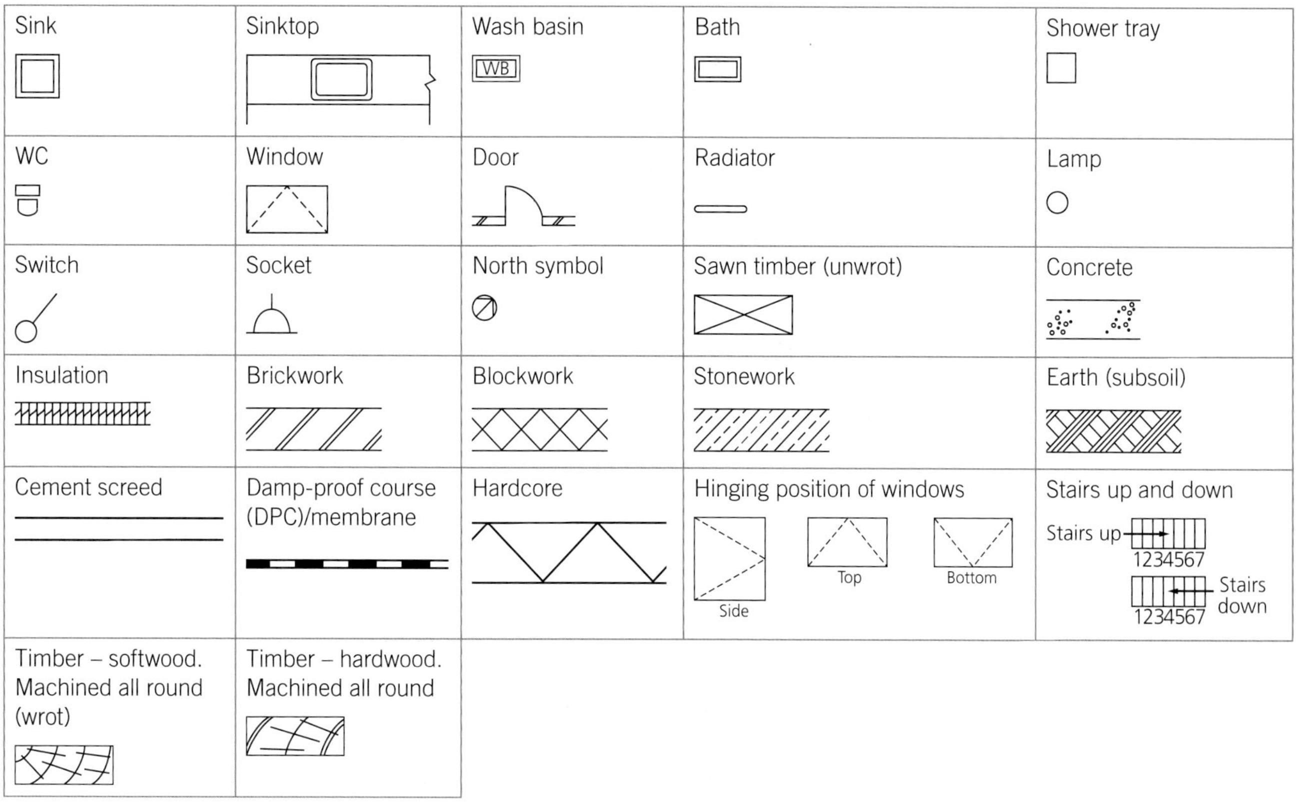

Sink	Sinktop	Wash basin	Bath	Shower tray
WC	Window	Door	Radiator	Lamp
Switch	Socket	North symbol	Sawn timber (unwrot)	Concrete
Insulation	Brickwork	Blockwork	Stonework	Earth (subsoil)
Cement screed	Damp-proof course (DPC)/membrane	Hardcore	Hinging position of windows Side Top Bottom	Stairs up and down Stairs up 1234567 Stairs down 1234567
Timber – softwood. Machined all round (wrot)	Timber – hardwood. Machined all round			

▲ Figure 3.9 Basic drawing symbols and hatchings

Drawings also contain standardised abbreviations. For example, RWP indicates a rainwater pipe, BIG specifies a back inlet gully and OPC refers to ordinary Portland cement.

ACTIVITY

Search online for 'construction abbreviations UK' and see how many there are.

Documents

While drawings are an effective visual method of communicating a great deal of information, a range of written documents are also necessary for a construction project to run smoothly. The main documents that link with plans and drawings to provide comprehensive information about a work task are specifications and schedules.

- The specification is a contract document, which means it is legally binding. It is used in conjunction with drawings, which can also be contract documents. Giving written instructions in a separate document prevents the drawing from getting cluttered with text (although some drawings may have a small specification panel at the side to give necessary details for quick reference). The specification gives information about the types and quality of materials to be used. It may also describe the work practices that must be employed for a specific job, to achieve the required quality of finish.

INDUSTRY TIP

Drawings and documents are referred to frequently when working on site, in potentially damp and dirty conditions. Keep these important sources of information in good condition by putting them in protective folders.

- A schedule is mainly used on larger sites where there might be several building designs, with each type having different components and fittings. It is usually used in conjunction with drawings. For example, a typical drawing will have doors and windows labelled D1, D2, W1, W2, and so on. These labelled components are then listed in the schedule along with other information. Using a schedule makes it less confusing when identifying repetitive details. It allows the listed components or features to be clearly linked to specific work tasks in different site locations.

2 THE PLANNING PROCESS

The local planning authority (LPA) is involved in development management, which regulates land use and new building projects. The Planning Policy Wales (PPW) document has been provided to 'ensure that the planning decisions taken in Wales, no matter how big, or how small, are going to improve the lives of both our current and future generations'.

Planning authorities are also involved in regulating work on listed buildings. A listed building is a building, object or structure that has been deemed to be of national importance in terms of architectural or historic interest. It will be registered and documented to give legal protection. (There is more information on listed buildings later in this chapter.)

2.1 Roles and responsibilities

Development control officer

ACTIVITY

Research which documents are required to submit a planning application by visiting https://gov.wales/planning-permission

Before construction activities can begin, planning permission must be sought from the LPA (often referred to as 'the council'). Development control officers play an important role in this process, dealing with planning applications and providing advice and guidance to developers about how their proposals comply with the local development plan (LDP). The LDP is important when making planning decisions. It sets out the LPA's proposals and policies for future development and use of land in its area.

The development control officer performs a range of duties to make sure the LDP is implemented, for example:

- assessing planning applications, consulting with colleagues and informing planning decision makers
- making site visits to discuss developers' proposals and check that planning restrictions are understood and complied with
- advising architects, contractors, consultants and the public to inform them about planning policies and procedures
- working with heritage conservation officers in preparing schemes for conservation of historic buildings.

Heritage conservation officer

Many ancient structures and historic buildings are protected by law. The PPW mentioned earlier sets out the Welsh Government's objectives to 'protect, conserve, promote and enhance the historic environment as a resource for the general well-being of present and future generations'.

The sustainable management of historic buildings and structures is therefore an important part of the heritage conservation officer's role. To undertake their work, they need:

- comprehensive knowledge and understanding of planning and listed building **legislation**
- the skills to assess measures needed to safeguard heritage assets
- the ability to communicate effectively regarding applications for listed building status.

Heritage conservation officers help to protect and conserve buildings as diverse as houses, churches, lighthouses and factories. They work alongside local and national government agencies, as well as heritage and conservation groups.

Building control officer

Before work can begin on new buildings, extensions or alterations, structural drawings and specification details must be provided to show that the proposed development meets legal structural standards. The building control officer checks these details for compliance before approval can be given.

Once work has been approved and the job begins, the officer makes regular visits to the site to physically check that the work follows regulations. If the work is not up to standard, the officer has the authority to issue legal notices to compel the builder to complete the work properly. If legal notices are not complied with, there is provision to prosecute offenders.

To fulfil their role effectively, a building control officer requires:

- good communication skills and the ability to deal with professionals and site operatives
- comprehensive technical knowledge of current building practices and building regulations
- good problem-solving and organisational skills.

All the required information about planning permission and building regulations can be found on the gov.wales website.

2.2 Primary planning legislation and regulations

There are three pieces of primary legislation relating to planning in Wales:

- the Town and Country Planning Act (TCPA) 1990
- the Planning and Compulsory Purchase Act (PCPA) 2004
- the Planning Act 2008.

Under these laws, a range of different descriptions apply to applications for approval.

For each of the consent requirements listed in this section, failure to comply with planning legislation or building regulations can result in legal consequences. If work is not completed in accordance with the relevant legislation, the appropriate authority has the power to issue enforcement notices leading to court action.

KEY TERM

Legislation: a law or set of laws made by a government

INDUSTRY TIP

If a building control officer visits a site you work on, be co-operative and willing to listen to their comments. They are interested in preserving the good reputation of the contractor, as well as looking after the interests of the client.

ACTIVITY

Visit https://careerswales. gov.wales/job-information and search for 'building control officer'. How do you become a building control officer and what could you earn?

In the case of building regulations, this could result in fines being imposed. If the breach of the legislation is significant and not rectified within set time limits, enforcement powers are available to require the work to be demolished.

Planning permission

Outline planning permission

An outline planning permission application is submitted to establish whether a proposed development would be acceptable to the LPA before a final detailed proposal is presented.

As the name suggests, only an outline of the proposal is given, providing limited information. This might include factors such as the type of dwelling to be constructed, the number of buildings on a plot, the type of roof structure and any other factors that give an understanding of how the development will impact on the surrounding environment or community.

Reserved matters

After an outline planning application has been made and approved, there are usually details about a development that have not been finalised, such as:

- design features of a building that affect the way it looks, such as the exterior finish or the type of windows
- how the development will provide safe access to roads and pathways outside the site
- landscaping details, such as the design features of open spaces and planting of trees or hedges.

These are known as reserved matters and must be in line with the outline approval and any conditions that were attached to the permission.

Full planning consent

Planning considerations need to be fully met before full planning consent is given. The LPA will consider whether the project proposal is consistent with the development plan for the area. Issues such as potential traffic problems, the effect on the privacy or outlook of surrounding occupants and the impact on the appearance of the surrounding area will have to be satisfactorily resolved before building work can commence.

Variation of conditions

There may be circumstances where an application can be made for permission to change or alter something in a building design that has already been approved. This is known as an 'application for removal or variation of a condition following grant of planning permission'.

Permission for changes or alterations may be granted with conditions attached. For example, changes to the position of windows may be approved on condition that the window design follows certain requirements, such as being 'vertically proportioned'.

Separate regulations apply to listed buildings to which an owner may wish to make changes or alterations. These applications are made under the legal heading 'application for variation or discharge of a condition attached to listed building consent'.

Building regulations approval

Building regulations are divided into subject-specific 'Approved Documents'. For example, Approved Document A deals with regulations for structural safety. It is the responsibility of the person carrying out the building work and, if they are not the same person, the owner of the building to make sure that the project fully meets the building regulations.

The building regulations apply to most types of building work, so it is important to know exactly when approval is needed. The following types of project are examples of work that need building regulations approval:

- construction of a new building
- an extension to an existing building
- an alteration project affecting elements of a building that are specifically regulated, such as making changes to external wall finishes that affect permanent ventilation serving open fires
- work to repair or replace the foundations of a structure.

Listed building consent

If the owner of a listed building wishes to make alterations or demolish the structure, they will need listed building consent. This special form of control is intended to prevent unrestricted work on a listed building without the consent of the LPA or Welsh ministers. It is a criminal offence to carry out any work that has not been granted consent.

Types of work for which an application for consent should be made are:

- alteration or extension of a listed building which would change its character as a building of special architectural or historic interest (this includes any internal work that is proposed)
- demolition of a listed building.

Conservation area consent

LPAs have the power to designate any area of special architectural or historic interest as a conservation area, the character or appearance of which should be preserved.

The special character of these areas is not just made up of isolated buildings but is also expressed in the character of the areas. This could be the pattern of settlement, the organisation of space and building plots and the networks of routes, as well as the style and type of building, their materials and detailing. (Source: *Managing Conservation Areas in Wales,* Welsh Government, Cadw, 2017, © Crown Copyright.)

Consent will be required for changes such as:

- demolition of a building with a volume of more than 115 cubic metres
- demolition or removal of a gate, fence, wall or railings more than one metre high next to a highway or open public space.

ACTIVITY

Visit www.gov.uk/ government/collections/ approved-documents. Which Approved Document gives you information on fire safety?

INDUSTRY TIP

Working on a listed building often involves using skills and techniques that are becoming rarer. Learning heritage skills is an interesting area of construction work.

The demolition of an unlisted building in a conservation area without the consent of the LPA is a criminal offence.

Scheduled monument consent

Scheduling identifies monuments that are considered to be of national importance to Wales. They can take the form of earthworks, ruined buildings and buried remains. Archaeological sites and historic monuments form one of our most important sources of information about the past. Some sites relate to periods before written records were kept, so they may be our only source of historical information.

Consent must be applied for if any ancient monument could in any way be affected by proposed development. Even metal detecting on a scheduled site must have consent. In Wales, advice on managing ancient monument sites is available from Cadw, the Welsh Government's historic environment service. Cadw is also the body that determines applications for scheduled monument consent.

2.3 Heritage protection

As previously mentioned, some structures of special architectural or historic interest may be protected and preserved as 'listed' buildings. Listing is not a preservation order, but it is intended to help manage change and protect the building, its setting and its features from unsympathetic works that could damage its special interest. There are around 30,000 listed buildings in Wales, which are given grades to indicate the level of special interest or significance they have. However, regardless of their grade, all listed buildings are treated equally in the planning system.
The grades are:

- Grade I (one) – buildings of exceptional interest
- Grade II* (two star) – particularly important buildings of more than special interest
- Grade II (two) – buildings of special interest which justify every effort being made to preserve them.

ACTIVITY

Visit https://cadw.gov.wales/advice-support/historic-assets and explore the different types of heritage protection. Study the 'Understanding' section for each type of protection arrangement.

▲ Figure 3.10 This bandstand in Neath, South Wales, is a Grade II listed structure

If buildings do not meet the national criteria, 'local listing' can be a beneficial approach to providing protection to historic buildings of special local interest. Many buildings serve a role in maintaining local character and a sense of place.

Scheduled monuments were also mentioned previously, and in Wales there are over 4,000 examples of them, including Roman remains, burial mounds, castles and earthworks dating from the Iron Age. Cadw has the authority to make inspection visits to monuments to ensure that landowners are fulfilling their legal responsibilities to protect and maintain these historical assets.

Conservation areas in Wales are protected under the Planning (Listed Buildings and Conservation Areas) Act 1990. There are over 500 conservation areas in Wales that are an important part of national heritage.

World Heritage Sites are listed by the United Nations Educational, Scientific and Cultural Organization (UNESCO) as places that have international value and must be preserved and protected for future generations to enjoy and be educated by. There are three World Heritage Sites in Wales:

- Castles and Town Walls of King Edward in Gwynedd
- Blaenavon Industrial Landscape
- Pontcysyllte Aqueduct and Canal.

▲ Figure 3.11 Part of Blaenavon Industrial Landscape, which is a World Heritage Site

Many ancient buildings are places of worship that are still in use. To maintain and protect them in a similar way to the listed buildings arrangement, a system known as 'Ecclesiastical Exemption' has been established. This means that some religious groups are not required to apply for listed building consent to undertake work on their listed place of worship.

Religious groups exempt from listed building consent must have internal systems of control that provide a level of protection that is at least equivalent to those operated by the LPA.

3 THE STAGES OF CONSTRUCTION AND THE INSTALLATION OF SERVICES

Buildings and structures follow well-established stages of construction. Understanding the features of each part of a building and how they link together will help you to contribute more effectively to maintaining productivity in the workplace.

3.1 Building a structure

Buildings have been constructed around the world in many different ways and from a vast range of different materials over thousands of years, but every building has similar elements – a foundation, walls and a roof. There are two main sections of a building that these elements fit into:

- substructure – the complete section of a building extending below ground-floor level
- superstructure – the section of a building that begins above the level where the substructure ends.

In this section, we will identify the individual parts of a building that form the substructure and superstructure.

Substructure

Foundation

A foundation supports the building and transfers the weight or 'loadings' of the structure to the natural foundation, which is the ground on which it sits. As part of the substructure, the foundation is the main **load-bearing** part of a building.

After considering the type of building and the ground conditions it will be built on, the most suitable type of foundation can be designed. A structural engineer is often employed at the design stage to produce structural calculations, to confirm the ability of the proposed foundation to perform as intended.

Each type of foundation has different characteristics and performance capabilities, as shown in Table 3.5.

KEY TERMS

Load-bearing: supporting the weight of a building or parts of a building above

Friction: the resistance that one surface or object encounters when moving over another

Reinforced: strengthened or supported with additional material

---

▼ Table 3.5 Types of foundations and their uses

Type of foundation	How it can be used
Strip	Strip foundations are widely used for housing and small commercial developments. The design specification will state the width and depth of trench that must be excavated to suit the soil conditions and the weight of the building. A strip of concrete is poured into the excavated trench to a minimum thickness of 150 mm, according to the design. More commonly the thickness will be increased to 225 mm. The surface of the concrete should be levelled carefully to allow easier construction of foundation masonry.
Pile	Piles are essentially long cylinders of a strong material such as steel or concrete. They are used to transfer the load of a building through soft or unsuitable soil layers into the harder layers of ground below, even down to rock if required. This type of pile foundation is known as 'end bearing' and is effective when a building has very heavy, concentrated loads, such as in a high-rise structure or a bridge. A second type of pile foundation is known as '**friction** pile'. Support for a building is provided by the full height of the pile creating friction with the soil it stands in. The deeper into the ground the pile is driven, the greater the friction and load-bearing capacity. Installing piles requires specialist equipment and trained personnel and can be an expensive option.
Raft Hardcore / Foundation concrete	A raft foundation is often used where a strip foundation would be unsuitable due to soft ground conditions or where a pile foundation would be too expensive. It consists of a **reinforced** slab of concrete covering the entire base of the building, spreading the weight over a wide area. The edge of the slab is usually thickened as a support for load-bearing walls around the face line of a building. If any minor movement takes place due to poor ground conditions, the building is protected, since the whole foundation can move slightly as a unit.
Pad Brick pillar Pad foundation Steel column	A brick pier or a structural steel column in a steel-framed building will produce loadings concentrated on a single point. A pad foundation can be designed with greater depth and additional reinforcement to support this type of load. When a pad foundation is used to support a steel-framed building, it can have bolts cast into the top, allowing steel columns to be fixed to it.

KEY TERMS

Footings: the section of masonry from the concrete foundation to the ground-floor level; sometimes, the whole foundation is referred to as 'footings'

Fabric of a building: the structure or framework of a building

ACTIVITY

Bricks and concrete blocks are the main masonry materials used to construct footings. Research 'trench blocks' and write a description of this material. Think of one advantage and one disadvantage of using it for footings.

KEY TERMS

Compacted: firmly packed or pressed together

Joists: parallel timber beams spanning the walls of a structure to support a floor or ceiling

Since the foundation forms the lowest part of the substructure, it will be buried out of sight. The section of the building that emerges from the ground is usually constructed in masonry and is commonly referred to as '**footings**'.

As most of the substructure is buried in the ground, it will be frequently in close contact with moisture. If moisture is not prevented from entering a structure, it can cause serious damage to the **fabric of a building** and potentially cause health problems for the occupants.

To prevent damage caused by moisture entering the living or working area of a building, a barrier is installed in the masonry walls at a level between the substructure and the superstructure. This is known as a damp-proof course (DPC) and is in the form of a strip of waterproof material (usually polythene) laid in the horizontal mortar joint of the masonry. The ground floor is also protected by installing a damp-proof membrane (DPM) underneath it, in the form of a sheet of strong waterproof material.

INDUSTRY TIP

If your role on a project involves installing a DPC or DPM, take care to avoid damaging or puncturing this moisture barrier. Damage may not become evident until some time after the completion of a building, at which point it can be very expensive to put the problem right.

Superstructure

Floors

Floors are load-bearing elements of a building, carrying the weight of occupants, equipment and furniture. The loadings they carry can be transferred through the walls on which they rest or are attached to, down to the foundation and, ultimately, to the ground on which the building sits.

There are various types of floor, which are constructed using different methods. The design depends on the type of building and the potential load that the floor will be required to carry. Table 3.6 shows the different types of floor and how they are formed.

▼ Table 3.6 Types of floor

Type of floor	How it can be used
Solid concrete ground floor 	A solid concrete ground floor design is often referred to as a ground-bearing floor because the weight of the concrete slab and loads placed on it is transferred to the ground directly below. The concrete slab of a solid floor is sometimes referred to as oversite concrete and it is laid on **compacted** material. Some solid concrete floors are produced with a smooth surface using specialist finishing equipment as the concrete hardens. If the surface of the slab is left with a rough surface, it can be given a smooth finish later by applying a thin layer of sand and cement called a screed.

▼ Table 3.6 Types of floor (continued)

Type of floor	How it can be used
Suspended timber floor Joist supported on hangers — Wall plate Air flow DPC min. 150mm above ground level Honeycombed sleeper wall Slab on hardcore or blinding	A traditional method of constructing suspended ground floors is to use timber beams called **joists**, which span the outer walls of a structure. The joists rest on lengths of timber referred to as wall plates, which in turn sit on supporting brick sleeper walls built at intervals. Upper floors are all suspended in that the supporting joists are attached to or bear on the walls of a structure. There are several ways of linking the timber joist to the walls to produce a solid and stable result. Steel connectors and joist hangers in a range of shapes and sizes allow quick and easy installation of timber beams when constructing upper floors. Timber floor boarding, or timber sheet material such as a suitable grade of chipboard, is fixed across the joists to form the floor surface.
Block and beam floor	'Block and beam' is a method of producing a suspended concrete floor that can speed up the process of construction. It uses factory-manufactured concrete beams that span the walls of the masonry footings. The shaped beams are carefully spaced to allow dense concrete blocks to be positioned between them. Provided that the structural strength of the supporting walls is suitable, this method can also be used in upper floors, which has the benefit of providing improved sound insulation.

External walls

There are two main types of external masonry wall:

- solid walls, which can vary greatly in thickness
- cavity walls, consisting of two individual leaves (or skins) of masonry with a gap between them.

Both types of wall can be built using bricks, blocks, stone or a combination of all three.

The outer leaf of a cavity wall is commonly constructed in brick, with each layer (or course) overlapping the course above and below it by the length of half a brick. This overlapping is referred to as bonding, and the pattern created is known as stretcher bond.

INDUSTRY TIP

There are other brick bonding arrangements with names like Flemish bond and English bond, which are mostly used in solid walls. However, occasionally they can be used in cavity walls.

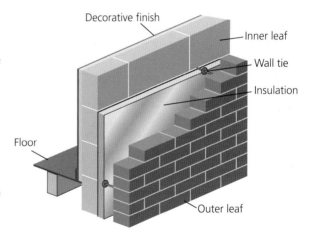

▲ Figure 3.12 Cavity wall

The outer leaf can also be constructed using concrete blocks, which will often be coated with a sand and cement covering known as render to give a smooth finish. Stone can also be used to construct the outer leaf of a cavity wall, depending on the design requirements.

ACTIVITY

Some cavity-wall insulation materials are not in the form of sheets. Search online for different types of cavity-wall insulation. During your research, what information did you find about the advantages and disadvantages of different types?

The inner leaf of a cavity wall is usually constructed using thermal blocks, to reduce heat transfer. The cavity between the inner and outer leaf is often used to install additional insulation in the form of sheets of special material to further reduce heat transfer. The leaves of masonry are strengthened and stabilised by installing stainless-steel wall ties across the cavity, located at specified positions.

Solid walls are less common in modern dwellings or workplaces. Older buildings built using solid stone walls are still in use but are often adapted using modern methods of damp protection. It is important that any adaptation of traditional buildings is carried out in a way that is compatible with their original design and construction. The design of cavity walls does not allow moisture to travel through them, making them the preferred option for external walls.

Openings in walls for doors and windows must be bridged to support masonry above them, and this is achieved by installing components called lintels. In the past, stone beams or hardwood timber beams were used to form lintels. Modern structures use concrete or steel lintels, which are durable and can also have insulation incorporated into them.

▲ Figure 3.13 Solid wall

INDUSTRY TIP

Steel lintels are often referred to by the names of the two main manufacturers: IG and Catnic.

▲ Figure 3.14 IG steel lintel

▲ Figure 3.15 Concrete lintels showing steel reinforcement

▲ Figure 3.16 Water moves off the top surface of the sill and is thrown clear of the cavity wall

The bottom edge of openings is also an area where moisture can enter the interior of a building. Sills (or cills) are manufactured in a range of designs using concrete, stone or brick, depending on the design requirements.

Internal walls

Walls within a structure can be:

- load-bearing if they support floors above them
- non-load-bearing if used simply as partitions to divide large internal spaces.

Internal walls can be constructed using timber or metal as a framework, ready to be covered in a material such as plasterboard or other suitable sheet material. Wall elements produced in this way are commonly referred to as stud walls or studding.

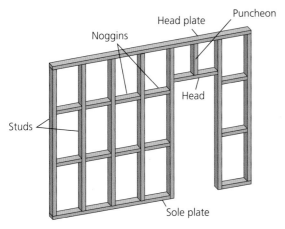

▲ Figure 3.17 Timber stud wall

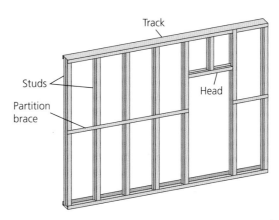

▲ Figure 3.18 Metal stud wall

When used for load-bearing situations, internal walls can be constructed using panelised timber systems to carry loadings, but are commonly constructed using blocks manufactured from dense concrete. Lightweight concrete blocks can be used, but this depends on the load-bearing requirements stated in the specification.

Internal walls (and ceilings) can be plastered, which means they are covered with two or more thin coats of plaster over plasterboard. In some cases, the plaster is applied over sand and cement render. This gives a very smooth surface which is then usually finished with emulsion paint or paper coverings.

The finish provided by emulsion paint will be more durable on new plaster if the surface is first sealed with a diluted coat of paint called a mist coat, followed by two undiluted coats.

Cladding

Cladding is the application of one material over another to provide a skin or layer. It can take the form of weatherproofing or simply be used as a decorative addition to the surface of a wall. Common cladding materials are timber, which can provide an attractive and sustainable finish, and plastic, which is durable and low maintenance. Metal cladding products are available, which are manufactured in a variety of profiles and surface finishes.

HEALTH AND SAFETY
Dense concrete blocks are heavy and need to be handled with care, using correct techniques.

ACTIVITY
Search online for 'external wall cladding' and list the different cladding finishes that are available.

Decorative features

Interior decorative features include:

- timber mouldings, such as decorative architraves around door frames and skirting boards
- plaster mouldings, such as coving or cornice used to embellish ceilings or decorative features applied to walls.

The design of manufactured items, such as specialist kitchen units, can add to the decorative appearance of the internal design, and even sanitary fittings in bathrooms can be designed to have an appearance in tune with the overall decorative theme of the building. Necessary drainage elements that remove waste water can be designed to be out of sight to preserve clean lines.

The shape of staircases and the design of the timber elements in the staircase can also be used to add interest. For example, the side timbers (called strings) could have a straight profile, known as closed, or be cut to match the steps. As well as serving the practical purpose of allowing access between floors, staircases can also have an architectural appeal by creating changes of direction as they ascend, turning through a quarter-or half-circle (referred to as winders).

▲ Figure 3.19 Quarter-turn stairs with cut string

Roofs

Roofs protect the structure they sit above by providing a weatherproof surface that directs rain to storm-water drainage systems. They must be strong enough to withstand high winds and the potential weight (or loading) of snow standing on them.

ACTIVITY

Wind is powerful enough to cause significant damage to a roof. Search online for images of wind-damaged roofs and note the extent of the damage that can occur.

HEALTH AND SAFETY

Because a roof is an elevated part of a building, it can be more exposed to strong winds. The hazards created by strong winds must be a safety consideration when workers construct a roof.

Flat roofs

A flat roof is not literally flat. It must have a slope or incline of up to 10° to prevent rainwater building up on the surface. Traditionally, the waterproof coating of a flat roof comprised felt material covered in tar (called bituminous), built up in several layers. An improved, longer-lasting covering is provided by layers of glass-fibre sheets impregnated with a special resin.

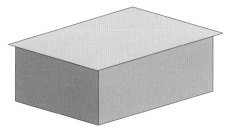

▲ Figure 3.20 Flat roof

Pitched roofs

A pitched roof has weatherproof surfaces that slope at more than 10°. They are constructed using timber beams called **rafters** and have a range of different design shapes.

A pitched roof can be constructed with a single sloping surface that leans against an adjoining wall, appropriately called a 'lean-to'. This type of roof is commonly used for porches and extensions to the main building. If a single pitched roof surface covers the entire building, this is referred to as a mono-pitch roof.

Where a roof has two pitched or sloping surfaces, with triangular walls closing each end of the roof up to the **ridge**, this is referred to as a gabled roof, and the triangular walls are known as gables or gable ends.

A hipped roof has no gables and the weatherproof surfaces slope down from the ridge to the tops of the walls on all sides. These roofs are more complex, and therefore more expensive, to construct. In an L-shaped building, where two pitched roofs are at right angles (90°) to each other, the angled line of the roofs where they meet is called a valley.

> ### KEY TERMS
>
> **Rafters:** beams set to suit the angle of the roof pitch, forming part of its internal framework
>
> **Ridge:** the highest horizontal line on a pitched roof where sloping surfaces meet

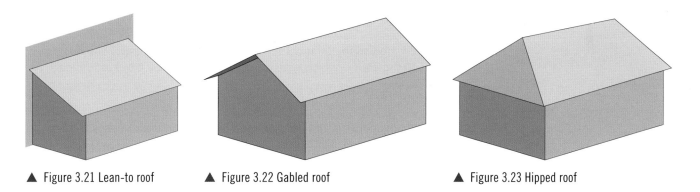

▲ Figure 3.21 Lean-to roof   ▲ Figure 3.22 Gabled roof   ▲ Figure 3.23 Hipped roof

Roof components

Traditionally, roofs were constructed on site from individual lengths of timber. These are referred to as cut roofs because the timber is cut on site to the required lengths and angles to suit the design. This is a process that requires advanced carpentry skills and a good understanding of geometry.

Study the hipped cut roof in Figure 3.24 to become familiar with the terminology used for roof components.

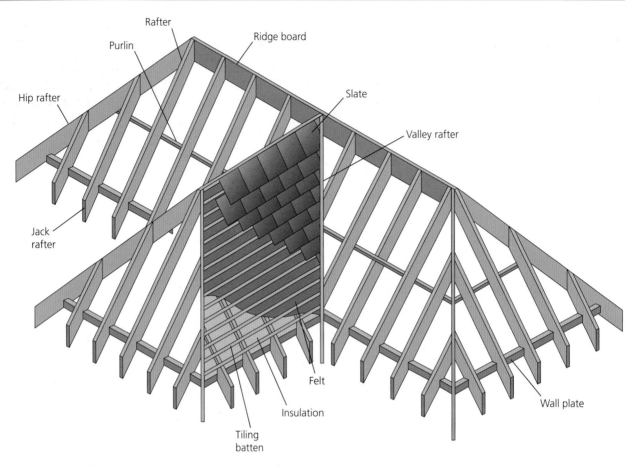

▲ Figure 3.24 Roof components

ACTIVITY

In Figure 3.24, how many different types of rafter are there? Each one has an angled cut on the ends – which type do you think would be the most difficult to cut?

Most roofs are now constructed using trussed rafters. This system uses factory-made timber components that are delivered to site and assembled more quickly than a cut roof, thereby reducing costs. This engineered system means that smaller-dimensioned timbers can be used, making additional cost savings.

INDUSTRY TIP

In a cut roof, the roof timbers need to support themselves as the roof is assembled so the individual timbers often have bigger dimensions than those used in trussed roofs and can be heavier to manoeuver.

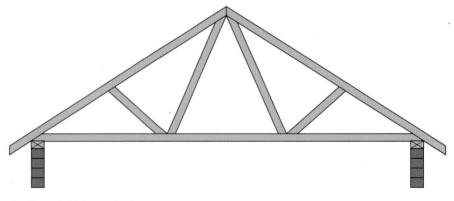

▲ Figure 3.25 Trussed rafter

Roof coverings

Once the roof structure is complete, a surface covering is installed, which must be highly water-resistant and durable. The surface covering is usually installed over a felt or **semi-permeable membrane** or sheet material that protects against windblown rain or snow entering the roof space.

Traditionally, slate has been favoured as a roof covering. This is a natural product which can be split into thin sheets by skilled workers. Slate continues to be used extensively as a roof covering, despite its relative expense.

KEY TERM

Semi-permeable membrane: a thin sheet of material that allows only certain substances (such as water vapour) to pass through it

▲ Figure 3.26 Natural slate roof covering

Tiles are an alternative to slate.

- Clay tiles are manufactured from a natural material and are produced in a range of sizes and shapes to suit different applications. They produce a finished roof covering that is attractive and durable.
- Concrete tiles are manufactured in different sizes, shapes, textures and colours. They are relatively quick to install and are often designed to interlock with each other to form a wind-resistant covering.

▲ Figure 3.27 Concrete roof tiles

Both clay tiles and concrete tiles are heavy components, requiring a roof structure that can carry the loadings adequately.

3.2 Sequence of tasks during construction

To ensure that work can be completed on schedule and within budget, careful prior planning of the construction process is required. This is key to efficiency and productivity on site. Planning a programme of work is often undertaken using charts to show the sequence of activities.

Each company is likely to have its own method of achieving this, but the principle is simply to lay out what takes place and when it takes place in an easy-to-understand manner. A Gantt chart (as developed by Henry Gantt in the early twentieth century) is a clear documentary tool that helps site personnel to follow a set sequence of activities and shows clearly if work on site is progressing to schedule.

Study the example in Figure 3.28. Note that there are occasions when a number of trade activities occur simultaneously. For example, during week 9, the carpenters, plumbers and electricians will all be working on site at the same time.

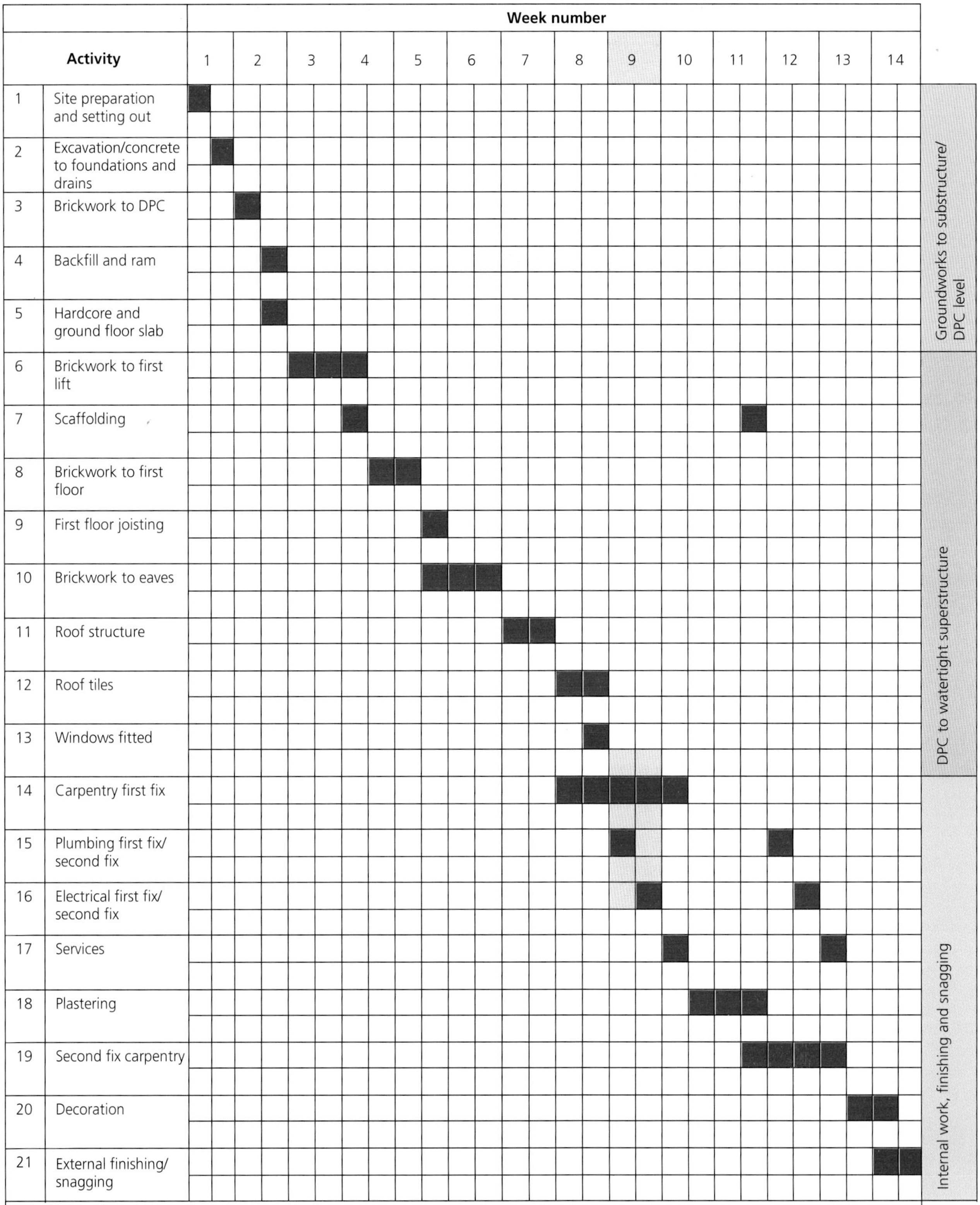

Activity		1	2	3	4	5	6	7	8	9	10	11	12	13	14	
1	Site preparation and setting out	■														Groundworks to substructure/ DPC level
2	Excavation/concrete to foundations and drains	■														
3	Brickwork to DPC		■													
4	Backfill and ram		■													
5	Hardcore and ground floor slab		■													
6	Brickwork to first lift			■	■											DPC to watertight superstructure
7	Scaffolding				■							■				
8	Brickwork to first floor					■										
9	First floor joisting						■									
10	Brickwork to eaves						■	■								
11	Roof structure							■								
12	Roof tiles								■							
13	Windows fitted								■							
14	Carpentry first fix								■	■	■					Internal work, finishing and snagging
15	Plumbing first fix/ second fix									■			■			
16	Electrical first fix/ second fix									■			■			
17	Services										■			■		
18	Plastering										■	■				
19	Second fix carpentry											■	■	■		
20	Decoration													■		
21	External finishing/ snagging														■	

Labour requirements

	1	2	3	4	5	6	7	8	9	10	11	12	13	14
Labourer	2 2	2 2	2 2	1 2	2 2	2 2	2 2	3 2	2 2	2 2	3 3	3 3	2 2	2
Carpenter	1					2	2 2	3 4	3 3	3		2 2	2 2	
Bricklayer		2	2 2	2 4	4 2	4 4								
Sub-contractors				x				x x	x x	x x	x x	x x	x x	x

▲ Figure 3.28 A Gantt chart showing the sequence of work over 14 weeks

This method of presenting information offers a clear view of overlapping activities and helps to identify when labour and plant requirements need to be met.

Note that the section for each task in the numbered sequence is split into two rows. This is to show actual progress against the planned activities. The top row shows the planned activity timings and the bottom row is a different colour to show actual activity timings. This allows easy monitoring and identification of any slippage in the programme (perhaps caused by bad weather) and steps can be taken to make adjustments to bring work back on schedule.

ACTIVITY

Look carefully at the Gantt chart in Figure 3.28 and identify how many trades work at the same time. Make a list of the overlapping work tasks that are planned and in which weeks they happen.

3.3 Effective and productive working relationships

In Chapter 4, we will expand on how interpersonal skills are needed to develop productive relationships and build team spirit on site as part of being employable. Good communication is a vital factor in exchanging important information effectively during both the planning of a construction project and the performance of construction activities on site.

Remember that everyone has the right to be treated with respect. To form good working relationships that will grow over time, treat others as you would like them to treat you.

Here are some points to consider when striving to build effective and productive relationships in the workplace.

- Speak to others in a tone that maintains their dignity – do not talk down to them. You might know more about a particular job that you work on together, but that does not justify acting in a superior manner.
- Behave in a respectful manner, treating others' property considerately. For example, if a colleague accidentally leaves a valuable tool on site, take the trouble to return it to them.
- If someone else is working on site in the same location as you, negotiate in a calm and co-operative manner to find a compromise that allows you both to get the job done.
- Build others' respect for you by being reliable, on time and clean and neat in your appearance.
- Maintain a good atmosphere on site by dealing with problems in a mature way. Know when it is appropriate to take a problem to your supervisor.
- Work with your colleagues to keep the workplace tidy. An uncluttered work area makes everyone feel happier.

The way personnel communicate with one another can affect motivation and morale on site, and respectful communication is essential if you are to play your part in supporting equality and diversity in the workplace. Showing respect and consideration when dealing with colleagues can also influence the reputation that a company builds with its customers over time.

▲ Figure 3.29 The construction team

4 PROMOTING THE SERVICES OFFERED WITHIN CONSTRUCTION

In Chapter 4, we will look at basic principles of business to see how a company makes a **profit**.

A company must make a profit to pay its workers and stay in business. Making sure that a continuous flow of work is maintained can be a challenge – it can often be the case that there is either too much work, placing a physical strain on the capabilities of a company, or too little work, causing financial problems.

Marketing a construction company is a way of boosting a company's profile to attract selected customers, build a positive image and maintain a steady flow of work.

4.1 Methods of marketing

Marketing approaches can be simple and economical or complex and expensive. They can use tried-and-tested methods or novel and creative strategies to engage new potential customers.

An important aspect of marketing is to reach out to existing and past customers. Soon after completion of a job, make contact to check the customer is satisfied with the work. Maintaining positive customer relationships is a powerful marketing strategy that costs very little.

KEY TERM

Profit: the difference between the amount earned and the amount spent when buying, operating or producing something

Traditional marketing

- Perhaps the oldest way of securing new business is to build a good reputation, so that people talk about the quality of work that a company produces. This is called 'word of mouth' and it can be effective within a small community.
- To reach a wider potential customer base, local newspaper advertisements can be used, if the interest generated justifies the added expense.
- Flyers can be used to good effect, distributed either by hand using employed personnel or by using the postal service. The costs involved in designing, printing and distributing them must be carefully weighed against the potential return in terms of business secured.
- Traditionally, phone directories featured paid advertisements for local businesses, but the use of these directories has declined.
- A more expensive means of advertising is to use radio. This has a broad reach and, by frequent repetition of adverts at selected times, a company's profile and reputation can be enhanced substantially.

Modern marketing

Modern marketing methods use sophisticated techniques to engage the interest of prospective customers.

- Targeted use of social media and online video channels can be an effective way of grabbing the attention of potential customers and can create a modern, vibrant image for a company relatively cheaply.
- The power of television advertising allows a company to engage effectively with local audiences. If marketing budgets allow, wider-scale or even national advertising can be a successful strategy to maintain and potentially increase a company's workflow.
- Many companies have a dedicated website, which can be strategically positioned in search-engine listings if the added expense involved can be justified. Even individual construction workers can benefit from creating a website to advertise what they offer to potential customers, and testimonials and references related to the quality of work can be presented effectively. A website can contain compelling video content about the work projects a company undertakes or interesting features about the team of employees, showing off the human side of a company. Getting to know a company's workers is an important way for a potential customer to build trust and confidence.

ACTIVITY

Search online for '50 construction industry websites UK'. Scroll through the websites you find and choose the one you like the most. What is it about your selection that appealed to you?

4.2 The impact of successful marketing on business

Successful marketing can positively impact on businesses of all sizes in a number of ways.

- Enhancing a company's reputation through advertising can lead to increased profits, with benefits to employers, workers and investors. Improved profits lead to increased tax revenues, contributing to local and national economies.
- Increased business gives the opportunity to raise employment levels and improve working conditions. Better office accommodation, improved IT systems and better-quality tools and equipment all depend on maintaining healthy profits related to a continuous flow of work.
- Reaching out to wider audiences may bring work enquiries that offer the opportunity to diversify into new fields of operation.

5 TYPES AND PURPOSES OF MAINTENANCE OF BUILDINGS AND STRUCTURES

A building is constantly subjected to persistent forces and loadings that can cause deterioration and damage. The effects of harsh and changeable weather, along with day-to-day wear and tear through use, can affect a structure over time, so proper scheduled maintenance and necessary repair or restoration work must be carried out. Addressing issues as soon as they occur can help to prevent much more serious and costly problems later on.

5.1 Types of servicing maintenance and repairs

Maintenance and repair of buildings can take two forms:

- planned or preventive – carried out to avoid the building falling into disrepair or the equipment within it wearing out
- unplanned or responsive – carried out after a fault or accidental damage has unexpectedly occurred.

Planned or preventive maintenance can take the form of service plans, which schedule maintenance at timed intervals. Examples include:

- servicing of gas appliances, such as central heating boilers
- testing of electrical appliances and circuits
- testing of air-conditioning systems.

The potential consequences of not keeping to maintenance schedules are detailed later in this chapter.

Repair of buildings takes place to deal with deterioration or accidental damage. Repairs and alterations may also be necessary when a building is

INDUSTRY TIP

Some construction companies exclusively perform maintenance work as a specialism. In large towns and cities, there is a continuing need to maintain buildings and infrastructure to sustain the efficient operation of the built environment.

subject to a change of use, such as converting a building for food packing, where hygienic conditions must be created in a structure previously used for other unrelated purposes.

If new features need to be fitted within an existing structure, such as upgrading of bathroom facilities or installation of new heating systems, there may be a requirement to alter or repair elements of the main structure to accommodate the new facilities.

There are specific repair tasks that arise that will be dealt with by different trade operatives working in construction trades and building-services engineering.

Construction trades
Wood occupations

A carpenter will remove damaged timber items and replace them with sound timber materials. This may require temporary support of structural elements surrounding or above the damaged timber.

Different types of damage or deterioration can occur in timber components.

- Rot is the decay of wood. There are two types of rot that can seriously damage the structural strength of timber:
  - dry rot – decay caused by a species of **fungus** that digests the part of the timber that gives it strength and stiffness
  - wet rot – the fungus causes the timber to darken and produce cracks along its length, usually under a very thin layer of what appears to be sound wood.
- Untreated timber is prone to attack from many types of insect. This is known as infestation and can vary in severity from the appearance of small worm holes to complete structural failure.

KEY TERM

Fungus: organism that feeds on organic matter such as wood

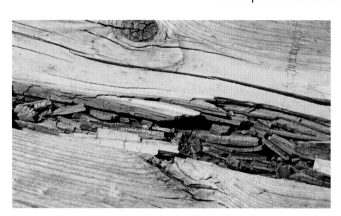

▲ Figure 3.30 Dry rot in timber

▲ Figure 3.31 Wet rot in timber

Timber used for structural elements of a modern building is chemically treated to resist attack by fungus or insects. When replacing damaged structural timber components, the carpenter should ensure that the replacement material matches the original.

Trowel occupations

Damage to and deterioration of masonry must be dealt with carefully, since bricks, blocks and stone are often the main structural components in a building. Frequently, removal of damaged masonry components will require provision of support, to avoid further damage being caused by collapse.

The following are examples of damage that those in trowel occupations will need to recognise.

- Frost damage – this occurs when saturated masonry is subjected to freezing temperatures. When water freezes it expands, creating pressures and tensions in the brick or block. Over time, the repeated cycle of freezing and thawing can break down the face of the brick or block and cause it to fracture. When the face of a brick or block crumbles away, this is sometimes referred to as spalling. Bricks or blocks damaged in this way must be replaced.
- Wall-tie failure – as mentioned earlier in this chapter, wall ties join two leaves of masonry in a cavity wall. In the past, wall ties were manufactured from **galvanised** mild steel or iron. The galvanising process (adding a coating of a metal called zinc) was intended to prevent corrosion and rust from attacking the metal ties. Experience has shown that this procedure was not sufficient to protect the component from deterioration, and wall-tie failure has proved to be a significant maintenance and repair challenge. Specialist methods of replacing defective wall ties have been developed to avoid demolition of large sections of a building.
- Cracking – cracks in masonry can be caused by a number of factors.
  - Large areas of a masonry wall can absorb heat from the sun, resulting in expansion. When the masonry gets cold, it will contract. This range of movement can be large enough to cause cracking.
  - As a building is constructed and the weight increases on the foundation, there will often be a slight amount of settlement. This can also lead to cracking in the masonry walls if they cannot absorb the range of movement.
  - The roots of nearby trees can cause the surrounding soil to shrink or expand, depending on the moisture levels. This movement will create tensions and pressures (sometimes known as heaving) beneath the foundation of the structure, leading to cracking that can spread through the foundation and into the masonry wall above.

▲ Figure 3.32 Frost-damaged brickwork

▲ Figure 3.33 A 'tell-tale' crack monitor detects movement in masonry

Plastering

Plasterers may need to repair damage to coatings applied to interior and exterior wall surfaces.

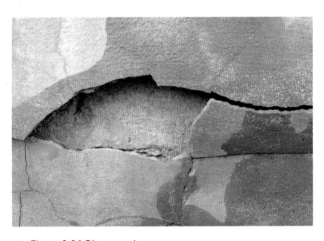

▲ Figure 3.34 Blown render

- A plasterer can apply a sand and cement mix called render as a finish to masonry walls. It is usually applied as a number of layers (or coats), depending on the specification. Cracking in render can be caused if the sand/cement mix ratio has too high a cement content, making it stronger than the backing masonry. The different rates of expansion and contraction in the render and the backing masonry will cause the render to separate from the masonry wall. If water enters the thin gap that forms, it may freeze and expand, pushing the render completely away from the masonry. This is known as blown render.

- Plaster applied to interior walls can be damaged if sharp or hard items impact its surface. Damage can also occur if plaster does not key (or stick) correctly due to an unsuitable environment during application, such as excessively low temperatures or contaminants present on the surface of the wall.

Roofing

Roofers can repair storm damage caused by winds or mechanical damage caused by impact from objects, such as falling branches or other debris.

- Flat-roof coverings can be damaged by being walked on repeatedly, although some types may simply break down over time with the effects of the weather causing cracks or tears. This allows rainwater to penetrate, causing further damage to the roof structure. A roofer will repair sections of the covering or replace the covering entirely.
- As mentioned earlier in this chapter, pitched-roof coverings can take the form of slates or tiles. Techniques can be used to replace single slates or tiles without damage to adjoining parts of the roof covering.
- A roofer may also undertake repairs to waterproofing components called flashings. These are usually made from lead, a soft metal that can be shaped (or dressed) to closely fit the location where a chimney projects through a roof surface or other areas where the roof shape makes it difficult to provide protection from the weather.

▲ Figure 3.35 Renewing lead flashings

ACTIVITY

Flashings are often formed from a soft, workable metal called lead. Search online to find out what other materials flashings are made from.

Civil-engineering operations

Structures in civil-engineering projects are frequently constructed in steel or concrete or a combination of both. Steel can rust or corrode and concrete can suffer damage or deterioration due to the effects of persistent moisture saturation, extreme temperature fluctuations or unintended structural loadings.

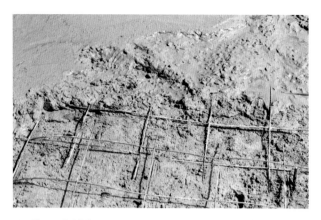

▲ Figure 3.36 Concrete poured over replacement reinforcement

Existing wall

Adjustable prop

Timbering

Failed foundation

New block foundation wall

New footing

Sand and cement packing between wall and foundation

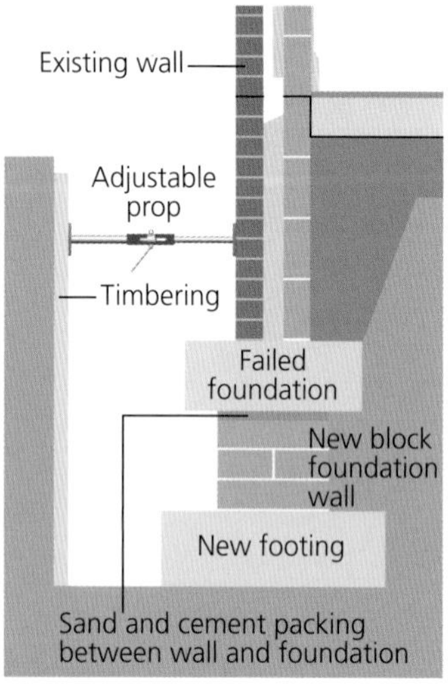

▲ Figure 3.37 Section view of a foundation being underpinned

- Steel components can be repaired or replaced by bolting or welding new sections into place where required. If steel is embedded in concrete as reinforcement and is subject to damage and deterioration, it is more difficult to repair. The whole section or component may have to be replaced.
- Concrete can be patched or refinished where appropriate, depending on the reason for the damage. The repair should be made in such a way that the possibility of future repeat deterioration is minimised.
- As mentioned previously, a cause of masonry cracking can be settlement or **subsidence** causing the foundation of a structure to move downwards, affecting the masonry wall bearing on it. A method of dealing with this fault and the associated damage to masonry is to use a civil-engineering process called underpinning. This involves supporting the foundation to prevent or limit further movement by stabilising the failed or damaged foundation. Excavations below the affected foundation are made a section at a time, and an additional specified concrete foundation is installed underneath to support it.

KEY TERM

Subsidence: a gradual sinking or downward movement of material beneath a building

ACTIVITY

Search online for civil engineering structures using cast and wrought iron. Research the difference in production process between these two types of iron.

Painting and decorating

Repairs involving painters and decorators are usually related to cosmetic damage to finished surfaces.

- Surfaces can be repainted so that the new work blends in with existing paint finishes. Similarly, with skilled attention, paper and fabric wall coverings can be repaired or, if the damage is too extensive, the covering can be removed completely and replaced.
- Water damage to decorated surfaces from leaks or water entry through a faulty roof can cause extensive damage that will require expert attention.
- General wear and tear can cause damage or deterioration to vulnerable locations, such as corner points of walls and doorway surrounds.

Building-services engineering
Plumbing, heating and ventilation

Leaks in plumbing systems can cause extensive water damage in a property and must be dealt with urgently. A plumber also deals with internal problems that occur when items are subject to wear, such as replacing toilet-flushing mechanisms or leaking tap seals. Internal domestic drainage systems can periodically require unblocking or cleaning to prevent flooding.

> **ACTIVITY**
>
> Look online for images of plumbing leaks. Leaking water can quickly cause serious damage to the interior of a building. Do you know how to shut off the water supply in your home? Find out where the water supply enters the place where you live.

External problems that must be dealt with include leaking guttering or blocked drains. Where external vent pipes pass through roof surfaces, the weather seal may break down over time and require repair or replacement.

Plumbers are skilled operatives who work with technical details related to water pressure and flow rates, storage-tank capacities and thermal-heating requirements. Some operatives progress to specialise in working with heating and ventilation systems.

Regular servicing of heating appliances must be undertaken by heating engineers who have been certified to work with the specific fuel used. Gas and oil are common fuels that require specific expertise, and training must be updated and certified at regulated intervals.

Heating and ventilation systems require understanding of engineering principles and technical information to service and repair components such as boilers, flues, fuel-supply systems or, in the case of ventilation systems, air-handling equipment and potentially refrigeration units.

Electrical

Damaged electrical systems can cause injury or death to people who come into contact with them, and they also have the potential to cause fires. Repairing electrical faults safely must be done by trained electricians who are certified to carry out work on electrical circuits and equipment. They must be familiar with methods of isolating electrical circuits, so that repair work can proceed while maintaining electrical supply to unaffected areas of a building.

Regular testing can highlight faults before they deteriorate further to become a risk to life and property. Equipment to protect users such as a residual current device (RCD) must be installed correctly and tested regularly to provide the required level of protection. RCDs cut the power immediately if a fault develops that creates a risk of electrocution.

5.2 The purpose of servicing and maintenance

Repairs to structures, services and appliances are carried out as a response to damage that has occurred – due to either an unexpected event or wear and tear.

Servicing and maintenance are planned activities that are preventive. This means that they reduce the likelihood of damage to components or failure of equipment.

Safety, security and economy are benefits of servicing and maintenance.

Safety

Regular servicing of heating and ventilation and electrical systems maintains their efficient functioning. This is vital for many reasons, such as the following.

- Heating systems produce dangerous gases during operation that must be conducted out of a living or working area through a well-designed flue or chimney. If heating appliances are not serviced, they can produce toxic gases such as carbon monoxide – an invisible, tasteless and odourless gas which can be deadly to occupants.
- Inefficient heating appliances also produce more deposits inside a flue, slowing the rate at which a gas is conducted safely away. Regular servicing and cleaning of flues and chimneys is therefore vital.
- The fuel used in any heating appliance is flammable and potentially poisonous, and leaks can be dangerous. As well as the effect on human health, there is a risk of fire or explosion. Gas leaks can lead to devastating destructive consequences, so regular servicing to maintain the integrity and reliability of the fuel supply to appliances is essential.
- Electricity poses a risk of injury and can kill in an instant, so servicing of electrical systems is essential to maintain their safety. Regular servicing applies to portable power tools and equipment, as well as permanent electrical installations. Regular portable appliance testing (PAT) is required under health and safety regulations. (There is more information on this in Chapter 5.)

ACTIVITY
The official website of Gas Safe at www.gassaferegister.co.uk has a register of all qualified gas engineers. Visit the website and read the section on carbon monoxide poisoning.

Security

Telecommunication systems form an important part of security. Many domestic and commercial alarm systems are able to automatically summon assistance from the emergency services. Servicing, testing and maintenance of these systems will ensure they operate as intended during an emergency situation.

Alarm and locking systems are becoming increasingly complex, requiring a high level of technical competence to manage and check their operation.

Economy

An efficient appliance uses less energy and will function with greater reliability over its working life. Regular servicing and maintenance extend the life of appliances and systems and make financial sense, both domestically and commercially.

> **INDUSTRY TIP**
>
> Because servicing and maintenance are so important, appliances should be sited in easy-to-access locations.

▲ Figure 3.38 Servicing a heating appliance

⑥ REPURPOSING OF BUILDINGS AND STRUCTURES

Construction of a building involves substantial investment in terms of materials, manufactured components, skilled labour and time. Imagination and creativity may also have been invested to create a building of visual interest, which can become a familiar feature of everyday life for many generations.

Society's needs change over time, and even attractive familiar buildings outlive their usefulness. At this point in the life cycle of a valuable building, there is the opportunity to protect and enhance the original investment by **repurposing** it – reinstating its usefulness as part of the built environment.

> **KEY TERM**
>
> **Repurposing:** adapting for new uses while retaining valuable features

6.1 Repurposing and reinstating of buildings and structures

Repurposing an existing building can be an attractive alternative to demolishing the structure and constructing something new. As we discussed in Chapter 1, the built environment we see around us has developed over many years and the disruption and disturbance of destroying a familiar part of it, such as an old building, can be avoided by repurposing.

Reasons for repurposing

Older buildings often play an important role in linking the modern era to historical architectural character and cultural heritage. However, there are also sound practical reasons for considering the repurposing of a building.

- Adapting an established structure for a new purpose can support sustainability, since a substantial part of the existing fabric of the building will be reused. Depending on the repurposing design, fewer new materials will be required, which translates into less energy being consumed during manufacture. The established connections to existing infrastructure can be utilised by a repurposed building.
- Demolition costs can be high as it is a specialist activity, so the repurposing of a building offers the benefit of considerable cost savings, since the main structure will be preserved. In addition, demolition of any building creates health hazards for surrounding communities due to the creation of dust, fumes and noise pollution that can only be controlled to a limited degree.

Older buildings in good structural condition can often be repurposed without major alteration, simply by refurbishing them or upgrading outdated services or internal systems. This could include:

- installing modern heating systems and boilers
- upgrading insulation
- rewiring electrical systems
- installing internet access
- installing alarm systems.

However, not all buildings can be repurposed. The physical condition of an existing building may have deteriorated due to lack of maintenance or neglect and the cost of upgrading it may be too high. The design of the structure may make it unsuitable to be adapted for other uses. For example, a prison building which is by nature split into small compartments would require extensive costly modification.

Change of use examples
Commercial buildings

Buildings used for profit-making activities can change use to become larger (or smaller) commercial businesses or be converted for domestic use as dwellings. An example would be a barn being converted into residential accommodation.

On a larger scale, a single large shopping facility could be adapted to become many smaller shopping units, increasing flexibility of use and offering shoppers a wider range of commodities.

Single to multiple occupancy

A single large dwelling can be adapted to offer multiple occupancy by creating individual dwellings within the larger structure. This often happens with large Victorian properties that have become too expensive to operate and maintain for single occupancy. By converting such a building for multiple occupancy, its architectural features can be preserved to enhance the character and attractiveness of the built environment.

Cultural buildings

Museums, libraries and older hospitals are often historically interesting buildings that were built in architectural styles that have cultural importance. If they no longer serve their original purpose, it can be beneficial to repurpose them for other public uses, such as centres of learning or community hubs. Some large cultural buildings have been adapted for use as apartments, often producing desirable residences.

As buildings of cultural significance, churches can be impressive structures that have an important place in the architectural landscape as community landmarks. Once they are no longer required as places of worship, these often substantial buildings can be adapted as multiple-occupancy dwellings, rather than being abandoned or demolished.

▲ Figure 3.39 This historic church is now an indoor marketplace

ACTIVITY

Are there any examples of buildings that have been repurposed near where you live? Try to find some when you travel around. Search online for examples of repurposed buildings.

Industrial buildings

Older factories and warehouses are spacious structures that lend themselves to being adapted for use as leisure and sports facilities. If they are repurposed with a flexible design, they can be enjoyed by multiple interest groups across the wider community.

During the Industrial Revolution, many industrial buildings were sited alongside transport infrastructure, such as rivers, canals and docks. Buildings from this era often have great character and interesting architectural features, which enhance their appearance when repurposed as residential apartments.

▲ Figure 3.40 Old warehouses converted into modern apartments

6.2 Recycling and reuse

Protecting natural resources and reducing carbon emissions is a continuing focus in all construction activities. The principles of recycling and reuse are highly relevant to repurposing buildings and structures.

Whenever an older building containing historic materials is adapted for reuse, there is the opportunity to recycle metal components and aggregates and to salvage items that are of architectural interest. Many modern buildings combine salvaged bricks, timber, slate and stone with contemporary materials, creating traditional design or cultural heritage elements that add a sense of place.

7 DEMOLITION AND DESTRUCTION OF BUILDINGS AND STRUCTURES

As mentioned earlier in this chapter, a building cannot be repurposed or reinstated if its condition has deteriorated too greatly, its location is not suitable or the extent of the work needed is too costly. Demolition may be the only viable option.

7.1 Requirements in decommissioning

Demolition is a specialist activity that requires careful planning and monitoring. Every demolition project has unique factors that must be identified by accurate surveys before work begins. When demolition of a building takes place in a town or city, the effects on the surrounding built and natural environments must be carefully considered.

▲ Figure 3.41 A water-cannon spray controls dust during demolition

Hazardous dust, fumes and noise will be created, and these must be managed to reduce harmful effects on the surrounding population and buildings. The health and safety requirements for decommissioning and demolishing a building are covered in detail in Chapter 5, but we will outline the basic requirements here.

- Control measures must be in place to ensure the safety of operatives working on the demolition project. Risk assessments and method statements applying to the specific project must be created.
- The safety of the public and protection of surrounding buildings must be planned for in advance of the work starting. Health and safety measures must be rigorously and consistently adhered to.
- The sequence of operations must be clearly planned and documented before work starts.
- Services to the demolition site must be isolated and decommissioned by trained and certified personnel.

When decisions are made on methods of demolition, safety considerations are to the fore. Dismantling structures involves dealing with heavy, bulky and awkward materials and components that pose a risk to the health and wellbeing of workers and the nearby population.

7.2 Methods of demolition

When viewing a demolition project in progress, it can appear chaotic and confusing. However, methods for dismantling a building and recycling or salvaging the materials it is constructed from follow well-planned and developed routines.

A range of demolition methods have evolved over time, with highly technical practices used for specific demolition requirements.

- Total demolition involves removal of the whole structure. The site is completely cleared to allow construction of a new building or reinstatement of open space.
- Selective demolition involves the removal of specific interior or exterior portions of a building while protecting the rest of the structure and nearby buildings. This can require pinpoint accuracy, so extensive surveys are undertaken to identify load-bearing elements that must not be disturbed.
- A structure may be dismantled or deconstructed piece by piece to preserve components for reuse or recycling. This is more labour-intensive and time-consuming than other methods, but it supports sustainability through careful extraction of usable materials.
- In the past, a standard approach to demolition was to use a large crane with a heavy steel ball suspended on a long chain (a wrecking ball). This was skilfully swung to collide with the building and dislodge large sections. Newer methods have replaced this approach, using excavators that operate with greater precision.
- Mechanical demolition uses specialised mechanical equipment and tools. Hydraulic excavators are equipped with attachments that can break or 'chew' concrete and steel (see Figure 3.42). Mechanised demolition robots can be used for smaller tasks where risks to personnel are considered too high.

- Implosion is a highly specialised type of demolition that uses explosives to collapse a structure within its own footprint or within a predetermined area. Explosives are expertly placed to undermine structural supports and initiate a controlled collapse.

▲ Figure 3.42 Excavators can be fitted with devices that 'chew' parts of a building to demolish it

ACTIVITY

Search online for 'demolition by implosion' and find videos of this method. There are some impressive examples!

Each method presents specific risks, such as the following examples.

- Implosion poses risks related to the use of explosives.
- Dismantling and deconstruction brings workers into closer proximity with potentially unstable structures because more work is done by hand, increasing the risk of workers being trapped or crushed by falling sections of the building.

All methods of demolition create potentially hazardous dust and some components produce fumes or gases when disturbed. For example, gas pipes may have residual amounts of gas in them after decommissioning, which may not be enough to create a fire hazard but could be breathed in by a worker.

Older buildings frequently contain materials manufactured from asbestos. This can cause a disease called asbestosis, for which there is no known cure.

When considering potential risks related to any demolition method, remember that risk assessments and method statements are vital planning tools in keeping workers safe.

HEALTH AND SAFETY

Safety measures may be in place and safety documentation may have been created, but if you work on a demolition project, take more than the usual personal responsibility for safety matters. This is an environment where hazardous situations can develop quickly, sometimes in unexpected ways.

7.3 Demolition waste removal

Removing waste from site during and after demolition must be done in a planned manner to prevent hazardous waste affecting the surrounding community. As a safety measure, the demolition site must be kept secure to avoid unauthorised access to contaminated or dangerous areas. When a building has major structural elements removed, what remains can be in a fragile condition and is a danger to the unwary.

▲ Figure 3.43 Removal of waste from a demolition site must be planned (note the security fencing around this site)

Security measures also play a role in protecting valuable reclaimed assets. Materials from demolition of a building that can be reused or repurposed and items that are salvaged for architectural use, perhaps in a new development, are increasingly sought after.

Often, a building due for demolition may appear to mostly consist of masonry or concrete. However, surprising quantities of different metals may be present within the structure. These metals may be valuable and can be salvaged or recycled. Structural steel columns, beams and lintels are often hidden from sight. Older buildings used pipework made from lead, or there may be copper pipes in more modern buildings. Cables that have valuable copper or aluminium cores can be recycled once insulation is stripped away.

Some demolition waste can be treated on site before removal, to make it more suitable for reuse. For example, concrete and masonry can be crushed on site to produce aggregate.

> **HEALTH AND SAFETY**
> Before removing pipes or cables, it is vital to check that services have been fully isolated and decommissioned.

▲ Figure 3.44 Crushing waste to produce aggregate on a demolition site

Thoughtful planning of a demolition project can reduce the carbon footprint of construction activities, support sustainability and reduce pollution and damage to the environment. Well-planned management of waste removal leads to less material being sent to landfill, which is a responsible approach that protects the natural environment.

Test your knowledge

1 Which tripod-mounted instrument is used for measuring horizontal and vertical angles in a construction setting?

   a Optical level

   b Laser level

   c Scanner

   d Theodolite

2 Which system collects rainwater for use in flushing toilets?

   a Grey water

   b Green water

   c Blue water

   d Brown water

3 If a building is designed to use standardised materials, how is waste reduced?

   a By reducing the quantity of items needed

   b By removing the need to cut components

   c By saving time when installing equipment

   d By avoiding using sustainable resources

4 Which type of plan or drawing shows the proposed development in relation to surrounding properties?

   a Site plan

   b Block plan

   c Detail drawing

   d Assembly drawing

5 What are the subject-specific sections of building regulations called?

   a Appropriate Documents

   b Appropriate Descriptions

   c Approved Documents

   d Approved Descriptions

6 Which type of foundation is used where the loadings of a structure are concentrated on a single point?

   a Pad

   b Strip

   c Raft

   d Pile

7 Which angle of slope describes a pitched roof?

   a More than 5°

   b More than 10°

   c More than 15°

   d More than 20°

8 What important benefit does successful marketing and promotion bring to a company?

a Fewer accidents

b More annual leave

c Continuity of work

d Tax reductions

9 Which type of maintenance is carried out to avoid a building falling into disrepair?

a Unplanned or responsive

b Planned or preventive

c Unplanned or preventive

d Planned or responsive

10 Which demolition method uses explosives?

a Total

b Implosion

c Mechanical

d Selective

Guided discussion

1 Describe three ways in which you can contribute to productive relationships between trade operatives.

2 Identify two things you can do to build others' respect for you in the workplace.

3 Suggest a situation when it would be appropriate to talk to your supervisor about a problem between you and another worker.

4 How can you promote equality and diversity in the workplace?

5 What do you think is an important factor in building positive motivation and morale on site?

CHAPTER 4

EMPLOYABILITY IN THE CONSTRUCTION AND BUILT ENVIRONMENT SECTOR

INTRODUCTION

According to the Chartered Institute of Building (CIOB), the construction industry provides employment for more than 2.3 million workers in the UK, making a significant contribution to national and regional economies. In Chapter 2, we looked at just some of the trades and skills that work together within this huge industry to create the built environment.

The wide range of work opportunities in the construction industry could make choosing a career seem challenging. This chapter will help you to understand the steps that can be taken on the journey towards securing rewarding employment. We will discuss which skills and behaviours must be developed in order for a person to be viewed by companies as an employable and valuable worker.

LEARNING OUTCOMES

By the end of this chapter, you will:
1 know about employment options and opportunities
2 know about employability skills
3 understand the basic principles of business.

1 EMPLOYMENT OPTIONS AND OPPORTUNITIES

Construction companies range in size and scale from single (or sole) traders, who take on small projects and employ skilled workers as and when required, to large organisations, which take on multi-million-pound contracts and employ hundreds or even thousands of workers.

The range of work opportunities available means that there are many options open to those who choose to work in this interesting and rewarding employment sector.

▲ Figure 4.1 An example of a small construction project

1.1 Employment contracts available in the industry

In Chapter 2, we looked at skilled workers in two categories: construction and building services. These workers are 'hands on', physically carrying out work tasks on the construction site.

▲ Figure 4.2 Workers in construction and building services are often 'hands on'

There are other types of worker who may be employed on site or away from the site in remote offices, for example, producing drawings or calculating quantities of required materials.

Roles in the construction industry can be divided into the following categories:

- professionals
- trade specialists
- general operatives.

Workers in these roles can be employed in the full range of construction activities, including new build, renovation, refurbishment and maintenance. Whether working for a company or self-employed, to be successful they need to maintain and improve their skills and abilities to meet the demands of a variety of work settings.

The construction industry offers many opportunities for career advancement. Most companies invest in their workforce by encouraging further education and study to gain valuable qualifications. Skilled workers are in great demand in construction, and the personnel requirements of the industry are often difficult to meet completely.

Once you have achieved a Level 3 qualification, you could study for a Higher National Certificate (HNC), or progress further to achieve a Higher National Diploma (HND) in construction. A construction degree is a valuable qualification, which can open up many career opportunities.

ACTIVITY

Search online for Higher National Certificate (HNC) to find out which construction qualifications are available.

Professionals

These personnel are trained and qualified to perform specific contract tasks. Training may involve many years of study in order to gain a recognised qualification. Some examples of professionals are listed in Table 4.1.

▼ Table 4.1 Professionals and the work they do

Job title	Work activity
Architect	Creates the concept and design of a building
Quantity surveyor	Calculates required quantities of materials and labour costs
Surveyor	Makes exact measurements and determines property boundaries
	Calculates heights, depths and other characteristics of a site layout
Civil engineer	Plans, designs and oversees construction and maintenance of infrastructure projects (note: this professional role is different to the civil-engineering operatives discussed in Chapter 2)

The qualifications that professionals obtain, and the level of responsibility they are able to take on, will often mean they work in management roles. As a result, they may enjoy higher salaries and other work-related benefits. They may be directly employed by a company or work on a self-employed basis.

ACTIVITY

Search online for other professional roles in construction, different to those in Table 4.1. Select two examples from your list and write a short description of their work activities.

Trade specialists

Workers who specialise in a particular trade or skill, such as bricklaying or carpentry, form the backbone of the construction industry. Successful construction projects require competent workers performing a range of skills. Many of these trade skills have already been discussed in Chapter 2.

The training of trade specialists usually takes the form of apprenticeships. Previously, an apprentice learned a trade over an extended period of up to five years. Nowadays, the training period for most trade skills has been reduced to two or three years, depending on the qualification level that the apprentice is working towards.

In the past, most skilled trade workers were employed by companies on a permanent basis with a constant rate of pay. This is sometimes referred to as working 'on the books'. In this type of employment, matters such as paying tax, holiday pay and National Insurance contributions are taken care of by the employer.

In recent times, workers are more likely to work as contractors or **sub-contractors**. Workers in this type of arrangement are mostly self-employed, which means they have an involvement with tax and National Insurance contributions themselves. They might also pay a contribution or **levy** to support training schemes for new workers. Payment for contract or sub-contract workers is often calculated based on price work (sometimes called piecework), where the rate is set for the quantity of work produced.

Becoming self-employed can lead to opportunities to improve your income and, with the necessary commitment, to set up a company of your own. For example, a self-employed trade operative who specialises in building extensions or high-quality construction projects could expand their work into a successful business.

Many skilled operatives have progressed to become employers in their own right and have made a valuable contribution to the employment opportunities of others.

General operatives

General operatives are often referred to as 'labourers'. They perform a range of semi-skilled and non-skilled work, for example:

- driving plant
- operating machinery
- assisting skilled trade workers such as carpenters or roofers
- looking after site storage facilities.

General operatives can work on a self-employed basis or be directly employed by a company. The smooth running of a construction site of any size is heavily dependent on general operatives who are reliable and trustworthy and who co-operate with colleagues.

1.2 Finding current job opportunities and apprenticeship vacancies in the industry

Planning a career in the construction industry can be made simpler by following these tried and tested steps.

1 Building confidence is a key part of becoming 'work prepared'. Personal self-belief can be boosted by taking advantage of work experience and work placement opportunities before entering training or paid employment.
2 Another important factor in becoming 'work ready' is making firm decisions regarding job choices. Think carefully about the type of work and career path that suit your preferences and abilities.

3   If possible, speak to individuals who work in the field that appeals to you, and weigh up their honest comments about the work they perform.

4   Build determination in order to succeed in training for and finding the type of work you have decided on.

5   Finally, learn how to use online job-search and research tools effectively. Be committed to sustained and thorough research – perseverance is a key factor to success in a competitive job market.

Research tools and techniques

Typically, a job website asks for the type of job you are looking for and the geographical area you want to work in. Filters are available to keep your search within a suitable distance from your home location, and a preferred earnings range is often requested. The nature of the job might be categorised under headings such as full time, part time, permanent or temporary.

The Careers Wales website is a good starting point in finding the route to your preferred construction career. It is funded by the Welsh Government and provides free and impartial careers advice. There are many pages of job descriptions, so you can find out what a job involves, the typical hours and pay, how to train for it and what future demand is likely to be. The website also has content on planning your career, courses and training, getting a job and apprenticeships.

The section on apprenticeships is comprehensive, explaining exactly what apprenticeships are, the different types available and how to secure one. A list of employers who offer apprenticeships is kept up to date, along with contact details for help and support. An apprenticeship scheme gives you the opportunity to 'earn while you learn' – an important consideration as you invest in your future.

Online resources can appear and disappear or change their focus quite quickly, but this government-sponsored website is likely to be reliable and well-maintained. Using online research tools is a fast and efficient way of accessing information about job opportunities, whether you want details about a particular company or to find out about work availability in your area.

However, do not completely discount the personal approach. Visiting your local Jobcentre gives you an opportunity to get advice on your chosen career path and assistance with finding work or training from trained advisors. Many companies with good reputations use government agencies like Jobcentres to advertise vacancies.

Before the advent of the internet, finding work often involved actually visiting construction sites to enquire about job opportunities. It can still be beneficial to speak directly to managers and supervisors on a site, if security measures and safety considerations allow this. Many construction careers have started this way.

Checking newspapers for 'situations vacant' or 'job vacancies' also used to be a popular method of finding employment opportunities in the past. This has become less relevant as publications have moved online, and due to the introduction and increased use of internet search facilities, which offer more opportunity to check different employers and work locations.

ACTIVITY

Search online for 'job-search tools' or 'jobs in Wales'. Many job websites require you to register before you can search listed jobs.

Find a website that does not require registration or setting up an account and try it out, so that you can get used to the way they generally work.

Choose a skilled trade and see what jobs are available. Then choose a professional role and search again. Make a note of the pay that is offered and the work location.

ACTIVITY

Visit the Careers Wales website at www. careerswales.gov.wales

On the homepage, click on the 'Apprenticeships' tab. Find the list of companies offering construction apprenticeships and write down 12 of them. It is surprising how many companies are listed.

113

Building a CV

CV is short for 'curriculum vitae', which is a Latin phrase meaning 'course of life'. It is a document that provides information about your.

- skills
- experience
- achievements
- character.

It also tells the reader how to contact you.

Taking the time to write (build) an effective CV is important. You want to capture an employer's attention as they consider whom to choose for a job placement, potentially from many applicants.

An effective CV comprises the following basic parts.

- Personal profile – introduce yourself and outline the qualities you have that fit with the job you are applying for.
- Current skills – try to focus on skills that the job requires.
- Employment history – list your previous jobs or work experience. If this will be your first job, list your achievements at school and any personal interests or hobbies that relate to the type of work you are applying for.
- Education – list your relevant qualifications and grades.
- References – provide recommendations and comments about you from someone you are not related to, such as a previous employer, teacher or tutor. It may be simpler to state 'references available on request' in the first instance.

There are many different types of CV with various layouts and appearances. Many templates and suggestions are available online.

ACTIVITY

Choose an online CV template and try building your own CV. If possible, print the completed document and ask someone in your learner group to comment on how it looks.

Application and interview skills

Completing a job application can be a challenging process to get right, but it can be made easier by applying specific skills.

Application forms that have been completed neatly and carefully create an immediately favourable impression with the employer. Untidy writing, poor spelling or grammar and crossings out may cause an employer to reject your application, even if your skills and experience make you a good fit for a job. Get comfortable at a table, use a good-quality pen and take your time.

In addition to providing your CV, it can be helpful to include a covering letter (some companies may actually request this as part of the application process). This gives you an opportunity to express yourself freely about why you want the job and why you feel you are suitable for it. This can be especially helpful if you do not have a long employment record to focus on.

Having submitted your application, receiving an invitation to interview is a cause for celebration but can also be a cause for anxiety. Again, there are specific skills and techniques to make the interview process less daunting.

You should always prepare carefully for an interview. Practise answering typical interview questions out loud, for example, 'Where do you see yourself in five years?' or 'What made you apply for this job?'. Try to predict what you might be asked and make sure you have an answer ready.

As well as stating what you can bring to the job, do not be afraid to politely ask what the job can offer you. An interview should be a two-way exchange of information; taking the initiative to ask questions shows an employer that you have given thought to what the job entails.

If you tell an interviewer something about yourself, such as 'I'm good at working in a team', give an example to build their trust in you. What kind of team have you been a part of? What did you do to contribute to the success of the team?

Your dress, grooming, speech and posture are vital in creating a positive first impression:

- dress smartly, not casually, making sure your clothes are clean and well-arranged
- avoid wearing jeans or brightly patterned shirts or tops; plain colours and crisp designs are best
- speak clearly, avoid slang expressions and never use bad language
- sit up straight, maintain eye contact and look alert and interested. You reveal a lot about yourself through the way you sit, stand and gesture.

ACTIVITY
Talk to someone you trust and make a list of the sort of questions you could be asked at an interview. Discuss relevant and appropriate answers to the questions you come up with.

② EMPLOYABILITY SKILLS

Having been offered a job or training position, you need to be able to work well with others and in a manner that your employer values. Working in the construction industry, you will often be part of a varied team, ranging from small groups of workers on small to medium-sized building sites to large teams of personnel on major projects.

Teamwork can be rewarding, but it can also present challenges. Team members need to be able to co-operate and communicate effectively.

Establishing and maintaining good working relationships between personnel in the workplace requires the development and application of a range of employability skills.

2.1 Behaviours and work ethic
Positive behaviours

Positive behaviour benefits everyone in the workplace. By dealing with other trades and personnel in a considerate way, you can maintain good working relationships. Everyone deserves to be treated with respect, and you should always treat others as you would like to be treated yourself.

▲ Figure 4.3 Treat other workers with respect

KEY TERM

Ethic: structured rules about behaviour, based on what is accepted as right and wrong

Being determined to do a good job and showing dedication to your work are part of having a good 'work **ethic**'. This is highly valued by employers. Let's look at some qualities that you need in order to demonstrate a good work ethic.

- Deal with problems in a mature way, knowing when to refer matters to your superiors. Taking the initiative can be a good quality, but assuming responsibility for issues you are not authorised to deal with will undermine your supervisor's confidence in you and can lead to resentment from fellow workers.
- Be flexible in your approach to work. Be willing to make adjustments to your work patterns if others need time or space to operate.
- Be professional in the way you plan your work, organise your activities and use your tools and equipment. Store materials neatly and position them considerately.
- Be diligent and observant regarding health and safety issues, to protect yourself and those around you.
- Be honest and trustworthy.
- Be reliable, on time and clean and neat in your appearance.
- If the company you work for carries out work for a private customer, look after the customer's property and protect their environment (for example, by sheeting over property that could easily be damaged and keeping the site clean and tidy).

Negative behaviours

Aggressive speech or behaviour can affect motivation, leading to reduced levels of productivity.

A slovenly, disrespectful attitude not only prevents you from building productive and happy working relationships but it also negatively affects the reputation of the company you work for.

Body language, such as facial expressions, can powerfully communicate a person's mood or feelings. These unspoken messages can have a negative influence on other workers. Examples include:

- rolling your eyes – perhaps meaning 'here we go again!'
- yawning – maybe indicating boredom
- hands in pockets – maybe indicating lack of interest
- crossed arms – a defensive stance indicating discontent with what is being said
- frowning – indicating doubt or disagreement.

Your body language is important when interacting and communicating with others on any construction project.

ACTIVITY

The next time you are in a classroom, look around before the lesson starts and see what you can determine about the mood of learners sitting near to you from their body language.

▲ Figure 4.4 Types of body language

2.2 Problem-solving techniques

The ability to solve problems and take the initiative within the limits of your recognised authority are valuable skills.

Problem solving can be described as a series of distinct steps.

1 Define the problem.
2 Determine the cause of the problem.
3 Identify potential solutions.
4 Choose the best solution and implement it.

It is important to carefully weigh up all the potential solutions before deciding on the best one. Sometimes, the solution you choose could create additional problems that may not immediately be apparent.

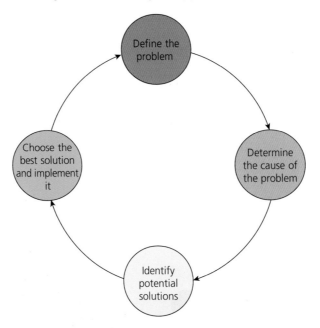

▲ Figure 4.5 Steps to successful problem solving

Let's look at some examples to see how these steps could be applied.

Problems related to time

Every work task on a site is given a timescale for its completion. A programme of work shows when the task must be performed in sequence with other activities, so that the work proceeds efficiently. If a problem with timing arises, it could be solved using the steps outlined above.

1 The *problem* is that the task is taking longer than intended.
2 The *cause of the problem* is that bad weather has slowed progress.
3 *Potential solutions* include:
    ● moving subsequent work tasks until later in the programme
    ● increasing workforce numbers to speed up the rate of progress
    ● substituting materials that are not affected by bad weather.
4 *Choose and implement the best solution:* increasing workforce numbers to speed up the rate of progress means that the programme will not need to be adjusted. Substituting materials that are not affected by bad weather could be expensive.

Problems related to space

Planning work within site boundaries involves making choices about the best use of the space available.

Decisions must be made about where to locate temporary buildings, storage areas for materials and access provisions. Unexpected events can sometimes create problems with the use of space on site, for example, an unscheduled delivery of large components.

1 The *problem* is that storage areas for materials on site are full.
2 The *cause of the problem* is early delivery of large items that cannot be stored in the current storage areas.
3 *Potential solutions* include:
   - cancelling the order
   - moving items out of the current storage areas to make room for the large items
   - setting up a temporary storage area near where the new items will be used.
4 *Choose and implement the best solution:* setting up a temporary storage area near where the new items will be used will not disturb the delivery timing. It will avoid having to remove items that are currently in the existing storage areas and has the added advantage of reducing the distance the large items will need to be moved to the work location.

▲ Figure 4.6 Storage area on site

Problems related to resource management

Resources on a construction site can take the form of:

- materials and components
- tools and equipment
- skilled personnel.

Managing all these different resources may involve problem solving. For example, specific requirements for machines and equipment must be met at different stages in the construction process.

Large earth-moving machines may be needed at the start of a project, followed later by smaller excavators or cranes capable of working in more confined spaces as buildings are erected across the site. If the correct machinery or equipment is not available at the right time, this could create problems.

1 The *problem* is that machinery or equipment is not available at the required time.

2 The *cause of the problem* is the fact that the contracted equipment supplier (who supplies all the hired equipment on site at low rates) has temporary transport issues.

3 *Potential solutions* include:
- cancelling the contract and finding another supplier
- adjusting the work programme to allow more time for arrival of the equipment
- finding an alternative supplier for just the required piece of equipment.

4 *Choose and implement the best solution:* finding an alternative supplier for just the required piece of equipment would mean that the work programme would not need to be adjusted. Cancelling the whole contract with the equipment supplier could cost more in the long run, because the low rates negotiated with the current supplier might not be matched by another supplier.

HEALTH AND SAFETY

Always pay careful attention to how the solutions you consider will impact the health and safety of yourself and others.

ACTIVITY

A problem regarding resource management could be a shortage of skilled personnel on site. Write down some solutions for this situation.

2.3 Team working and interpersonal skills

Working as a team is vital in construction. Section 2.1 above discussed how behaviours and attitudes affect the way a construction team works together. Continually analyse your own attitude and contribution to the team.

Although you may gain the respect of others as you become increasingly skilled in your chosen trade, always continue to co-operate with your supervisors and managers and recognise their authority. Many of them will have long and varied experience in the industry and they may have studied to advance their careers, so they should be given due respect in their responsible positions.

For work on a construction site to go smoothly, there needs to be co-operation and good communication between all personnel. Communication involves sharing thoughts, information and ideas. A breakdown in communication can cause misunderstandings and mistakes that can lead to wasted materials, time and effort. Poor communication can also lead to accidents.

Communication takes many forms, including verbal and written. Successful teams use effective communication in all forms to build trust, encourage co-operation, minimise negative influences and enhance positive qualities.

Verbal communication

Every day, we naturally use different methods to communicate without thinking about it. The most common forms of verbal communication in construction are:

- talking face to face
- talking on the phone
- using site radios.

▲ Figure 4.7 Verbal communication can occur in many ways

Mistakes can easily be made when communicating verbally. The person giving the information might not make the matter clear enough or the person receiving the information might misunderstand something. Often there is a lot of background noise on site, which can lead to information being misheard.

Since there is rarely a record of spoken conversations, it is sensible to remember these important points.

- Think before you speak, so that you get across exactly what you want to say.
- Be clear and concise in what you say.
- Ask for confirmation that what you have said has been understood.

Written communication

Written communication can form a permanent record of information passed to others. If it is read and interpreted carefully, it can reduce the chance of misunderstandings and allow reference to relevant information at a later date.

Sometimes, it may be necessary to communicate complaints or concerns in writing. This was traditionally done by letter, although nowadays it is more likely to be via email, which is delivered almost instantly and has the facility to attach scanned or electronic documents and drawings.

Electronic communication still needs to be written properly to be effective. You should take care to present information in a clear and logical way.

Here are some points to keep in mind when communicating by email.

- Help the person receiving the email to understand the urgency or importance of your message with a clear subject line.
- Keep your emails short and make sure your message is clear by avoiding phrases that could easily be misinterpreted.

- Use a spell checker before sending your message to avoid potentially embarrassing errors.
- Carefully read your email before you hit the send button. Would you be comfortable with someone other than the intended recipient reading it?

Remember that emails can easily be forwarded to others, so be careful not to write anything that could offend another reader.

IMPROVE YOUR ENGLISH

Draft an email to a supplier with the subject heading 'Damaged delivered materials'.

Explain that a recent delivery of six pallets of bricks (you can think of a date) had damaged bricks in the bottom two layers of each pallet. This could not be seen when the pallets were inspected during delivery. Ask the supplier to replace the damaged bricks.

Make the tone of your email polite but firm. Get someone else to read and comment on it.

3 PRINCIPLES OF BUSINESS

In Chapter 1, we discussed how buildings are of great importance to our everyday comfort and wellbeing. The construction of the built environment also has an economic impact on our society, since the companies that carry out this work do so to generate income for themselves and their employees.

Careful management of the business activities of construction companies is vital to their continued success.

3.1 Basic principles of business
Profit, loss and overheads

To stay in business and prosper, a company must make a 'profit'. Essentially, profit can be defined as the difference between the amount earned and the amount spent when buying, operating or producing something.

When working on a project, a company will spend money on things such as:

- paying the wages of workers
- obtaining materials and equipment needed to complete the project
- investing for future growth of the business
- paying taxes to support regional and national economies.

There will also be regular repeated costs associated with the day-to-day running of a business. These are called overheads and may include:

- purchase or rental of premises
- payment for services such as water, electricity, telephones and internet
- purchase or leasing of vehicles
- repairs to plant or machinery
- annual insurance.

If the amount spent on completing a project is more than the amount earned, the company will suffer a loss, which is the opposite of a profit. A loss-making company obviously will not be able to continue in business over a long period.

Book keeping

Careful record-keeping is essential for maintaining the healthy financial state of any business. Keeping track of funds that go out (expenditure) and funds that come in (income) is achieved by using established systems and processes known as book keeping.

IMPROVE YOUR MATHS

Make your own copy of the simple balance sheet below and complete the totals for each column.

Date	Description	Money in (£)	Money out (£)	Bank balance (£)
				On hand: 12000.00
31 July	Wages		2500.00	
1 August	Payment from client	15000.50		
3 August	Refund from supplier	150.00		
5 August	Purchase of van		10050.00	
	Totals:			

Manually writing figures in books to balance income and expenditure and calculate profit has largely been replaced by the use of specially designed computer programs. These often have the facility to quickly analyse and identify trends in the movement of funds through a business, which is referred to as cash flow.

Business growth

It can be challenging to simultaneously maintain a healthy cash flow and grow a business. Some small- to medium-size companies minimise individual risks and liabilities by working together (networking) with other similar-sized companies to take on larger projects.

The amount a company charges a customer will be calculated by establishing:

- the cost of materials needed
- the equipment and labour requirements
- overheads that must be covered over the duration of the project
- the **prime costs** involved when setting up the project.

The total of these costs is recorded and an amount is added on as profit.

The difference between the total costs and the amount of profit is called the 'profit margin', which is often expressed as a **percentage**. The percentage rate applied will depend on several factors, including:

- current workload
- competition
- complexity of the project.

KEY TERMS

Prime costs: payments that cover work undertaken by **nominated** sub-contractors, nominated suppliers and **statutory undertakings**

Nominated: chosen by name for a particular job

Statutory undertakings: the various services that are brought to the site, such as water and electricity

Percentage: part of a quantity expressed in hundredths

3.2 The importance of productivity and reputation

We sometimes hear in the media about large projects exceeding their original financial budget or failing to meet completion deadlines. When this happens, it can be very damaging to the reputation of a company. Potential future clients could be reluctant to employ a company that has previously failed in these important areas.

However, companies are not just featureless organisations; they are made up of many individual workers and you could be one of them. As mentioned previously in this chapter, all workers on a site need to monitor their personal contribution to the smooth running of a project and produce the best quality work they are capable of.

Building a good reputation can take a long time, but destroying a good reputation can happen very quickly if potential customers see that productivity and quality standards are not being maintained. A company with a good reputation is more likely to attract new customers, retain staff and make a profit.

3.3 The importance of customer service

To maintain a good reputation, a construction company must meet the expectations of the customer throughout a project.

From the time a company or sole trader is engaged by the customer, throughout the process of writing a contract to set out the terms of the work, a contractor must be clear about how work on the project is planned.

The customer should be provided with a clear view of:

- the timescales over which the work will be scheduled
- how much the work will cost
- how the company will request payment at specific stages of the project
- what documentation will be used when a request for payment is made (called invoicing).

ACTIVITY

There are many online templates for invoices. Find an example that would be suitable for use on a small construction project.

Work with a partner to complete the invoice to request payment for an imaginary work task that was completed in one day. (Examples of suitable simple work tasks could be removing rubble in a skip, painting a door, stripping wallpaper from one internal wall or anything else you can think of.)

These factors are an essential part of customer service. How they are implemented will affect how the customer views the company and what they tell others about the work they have paid to have done.

Good customer service also includes the contractor thinking about the reputation of the customer. Construction activities could cause disruption to the public, and the customer might be blamed for causing the nuisance. For example:

- deliveries to site could inconvenience others in the locality
- work activities might create noise and dust.

A contractor should plan ways to minimise such issues, to reduce negative perceptions of the customer.

▲ Figure 4.8 Construction work can cause a nuisance to others

Good customer service can be summarised as follows.

- Initial engagement – from the outset, the contractor should be specifically interested in the requirements of the customer.
- Pricing and quoting – the cost of the job should be stated clearly to avoid confusion. A firm price (or quote) must be agreed before work starts.
- Scheduling – the duration of the project and sequence of work must be set out clearly and realistically.
- Transparency – the working relationship between the contractor and the customer is more likely to be successful if there is honest and open communication.
- Quality of work – the contract and the specification for the project will establish the standards of quality expected by the customer.
- Considerate construction – it is vital to take account of the needs of the customer and how those living or working in the vicinity of the project will be affected.

ACTIVITY

The Considerate Constructors Scheme encourages contractors to be considerate of others during construction operations. Visit the website at www. ccscheme.org.uk and find the 'Code of considerate practice'. List the five points that a considerate contractor should strive to work towards.

A contract sets out:

- the expectations of the customer
- how the contractor will meet those expectations.

How the contractor fulfils the requirements of the contract will have a significant impact on their reputation and future as a profitable business.

There may be consequences for not fulfilling the contract, such as a penalty clause for not meeting stated deadlines. A penalty clause may involve the payment of large sums of money, which can have a serious impact on the financial health of a company.

3.4 The consequences of loss of business

If a company plans projects poorly or does not maintain high standards of work and customer service, it will be unlikely to continue as a profitable business.

The consequences of any resulting financial loss can be extensive and will affect many individuals and groups associated with the business. These consequences include the following.

- Loss of earnings – the personal consequences of workers losing their income are serious. For example, they may not be able to keep up with mortgage, rent or loan payments.
- Loss of **assets** – equipment and machinery owned by the company are examples of assets that may need to be sold to pay debts or to meet other costs. The working efficiency of the company may be severely affected without these items.
- Delay in growth – a poor reputation can result in fewer contracts being awarded. Without sustained and increased work, a company will not expand or grow.
- **Redundancy** of staff – if work levels cannot be sustained, it may not be possible to meet the cost of employing staff. Valuable staff members may have to be made redundant.
- Lower credit score – most companies use borrowing facilities from time to time to maintain their cash flow. If lenders become aware that a company may not be able to meet its repayment commitments because of loss of business, there could be an impact on its credit score.
- Late repayment fees – late payment of suppliers because of cash flow problems caused by loss of business could incur penalty fees, adding to financial difficulties.
- **Bankruptcy** – when a company can no longer repay its creditors and there is no prospect of an improvement in its financial condition, it may be declared bankrupt. Assets that are available will be sold to offset debt as much as possible.

KEY TERMS

Assets: items of value owned by a company

Redundancy: a form of dismissal from a job when employers need to reduce the size of their workforce

Bankruptcy: a legal process to deal with a person or business that is unable to repay outstanding debts

Test your knowledge

1 What do the letters HNC stand for?

   a Higher Named Category

   b Higher Numerical Certificate

   c Higher National Certificate

   d Higher Notional Credential

2 Which of the following might work as a supervisor or manager?

   a Apprentice

   b Labourer

   c Trainee

   d Quantity surveyor

3 Which term describes a payment you are obliged to make to support an industry training organisation?

   a Duty

   b Levy

   c Loan

   d Charge

4 Which group of workers are often referred to as labourers?

   a Trade operatives

   b General operatives

   c Skilled operatives

   d Craft operatives

5 Why is it important to spend time carefully writing a CV?

   a You need to be certain that you really want the job

   b You need to show that you can get any job you want

   c You want to impress the other people applying for the job

   d You want an employer to clearly see your employability

6 What does it mean to have a good work ethic?

   a Making sure others get the job done

   b Being determined to do a job well

   c Being the first to identify problems

   d Making sure you earn the most pay

7 Which term describes regular repeated costs associated with the day-to-day running of a business?

   a Overheads

   b Expenses

   c Outgoings

   d Payments

8 Which document is used to request a payment from a customer?

   a Claim

   b Invoice

   c Demand

   d Statement

9 Which term describes smaller companies working together to complete a large project?

   a Connecting

   b Balancing

   c Networking

   d Maximising

10 What is the legal process used when a business is unable to repay outstanding debts?

   a Complacency

   b Bankruptcy

   c Redundancy

   d Transparency

Guided discussion

1 Describe the differences between the work roles of general operatives and professionals.

2 When searching for work opportunities, what are the most important qualities you need to have?

3 Describe how you should behave towards others if you want them to co-operate with you and treat you with respect.

4 Describe the steps for successful problem solving.

5 Outline how you would deal with a dispute between you and another worker on site.

CHAPTER 5

PROTECTING HEALTH, SAFETY AND THE ENVIRONMENT WHEN WORKING IN THE CONSTRUCTION AND BUILT ENVIRONMENT SECTOR

INTRODUCTION

A career in the construction industry can be rewarding and worthwhile. However, it must be accepted that the construction environment presents many potential hazards, some of which have unfortunately had serious effects on the careers and lives of workers. All workers must develop the skills to identify hazards, assess risks and take appropriate action to keep themselves and others safe.

In this chapter, we will look at how safety laws and regulations benefit each worker and how you can apply them to contribute to maintaining safety and welfare in the workplace. Striving to protect yourself and those working with you offers the prospect of enjoying a long and rewarding career in the construction industry.

LEARNING OUTCOMES

By the end of this chapter, you will:
1   know workplace health and safety
2   know health and welfare considerations for working on site
3   understand principles of risk management
4   know the equipment and associated risks within the construction and built environment sector
5   know the principles of environmental protection.

1 WORKPLACE HEALTH AND SAFETY

The introduction of effective health and safety legislation, combined with the sustained efforts of workers on site, has made the workplace much safer than in the past. Everyone involved in construction activities has a responsibility to make sure that high safety standards are maintained. That includes those who write the laws, employers and workers like you.

1.1 The importance of health and safety

Personal safety

Many workers have thought that an accident could never happen to them. The reality is that many still experience the consequences of an accident each year.

Accidents can have a devastating effect on individuals and their families, causing pain, distress and anxiety, potentially over long periods. There can also

KEY TERMS

Compensation: something (usually money) awarded to someone in recognition of loss, suffering or injury

Induction: an occasion when someone is introduced to and informed about a new job or organisation

Toolbox talks: short meetings arranged at regular intervals at your work location on site to discuss safety issues; they are used to give safety reminders and inform personnel about new hazards that may have recently arisen, for example, due to extreme weather

be significant financial costs for workers due to lost earnings, and workers can be prosecuted and lose their job if they are found to have broken safety laws. Companies can have injury **compensation** claims imposed on them, affecting their profitability.

Site safety

Health and safety laws have been formulated to protect you and those working with you, from the time you first arrive on site and throughout each stage of your daily work routine.

- When you first arrive on site to begin a new job, you will be provided with important safety information by attending an **induction** meeting.
- When you need safety updates during working hours, **toolbox talks** will be arranged.
- When you enter and leave the site each day, laws and regulations are in place to protect all workers from hazards such as injury from moving machinery and vehicles.

An induction will alert you to important details such as:

- specific hazards on site that you need to be aware of
- the location of emergency assembly points, first-aid facilities and general welfare provisions
- site rules, including risks and penalties associated with the use of drugs and alcohol
- how to keep the site tidy and dispose of waste safely.

INDUSTRY TIP

You will attend an induction meeting when you arrive on site for the first time. Take a notebook with you and write down the key safety points that are discussed. Make a note of who the first-aiders are.

▲ Figure 5.1 Induction meetings provide important safety information

Inspections take place regularly on site, to make sure the many safety laws are being followed. The consequences of non-compliance can be severe and lead to closure of the site and prosecution in the courts. (More on this later in this chapter.)

1.2 Health and safety legislation

The range of health and safety laws and regulations in the United Kingdom is wide. The purpose of creating so many laws and regulations is not simply to punish those who disregard them. Rather, they provide the legal framework to promote and encourage high standards of health and safety on site.

The main legislation that regulates work on site includes:

- Health and Safety at Work etc. Act (HASAWA) 1974
- Reporting of Injuries, Diseases and Dangerous Occurrences Regulations (RIDDOR) 2013
- Control of Substances Hazardous to Health (COSHH) Regulations 2002 (amended 2004)
- Provision and Use of Work Equipment Regulations (PUWER) 1998
- Manual Handling Operations Regulations 1992 (amended 2002)
- Personal Protective Equipment at Work Regulations 1992
- Work at Height Regulations 2005 (amended 2007)
- Control of Noise at Work Regulations 2005
- Control of Vibration at Work Regulations 2005
- Electricity at Work Regulations 1989
- Lifting Operations and Lifting Equipment Regulations (LOLER) 1998
- Construction, Design and Management (CDM) Regulations 2015.

The purpose of each piece of legislation and whom it affects is discussed in the next section of this chapter. You are not expected to know every detail of this long list of legislation that applies to construction activities. However, you should be aware of the existence of each piece of legislation and its application in the workplace.

The Health and Safety Executive (HSE) is a body set up by the UK Government. It makes sure that the law is carried out correctly and has broad powers to ensure that it can do its job. It can carry out inspections, investigations and spot checks in the workplace. It can involve the police, examine anything on the premises and take things away to be examined.

The HSE provides a lot of advice on safety and publishes numerous booklets and information sheets, such as **Approved Code of Practice (ACOP)** documents. ACOPs have a special legal status, and employers and employees are expected to work within their guidelines.

Each person involved in the construction process on a building site must understand their role in maintaining health and safety and take their assigned responsibilities seriously. Remember, the HSE has extensive powers to ensure that all personnel comply with the appropriate legislation to keep everyone safe.

The law can be enforced by taking an employer, employee, self-employed person or anyone else involved with the building process (including the client) to court and prosecuting them for breaking health and safety legislation.

> **INDUSTRY TIP**
>
> Although the amount of health and safety legislation may make it seem like construction sites are extremely dangerous places, there is no need to be anxious about working in construction. Just follow the instructions and guidelines carefully and you will protect yourself and others from harm.

> **KEY TERM**
>
> **Approved Code of Practice (ACOP):** a set of written directions and methods of work, issued by an official body or professional association and approved by the HSE, that provides practical advice on how to comply with the law

The HSE can also issue:

- an improvement notice, where changes need to be made to comply with the law
- a prohibition notice, where unsafe work practices or the use of unsafe equipment cannot be allowed to continue.

1.3 Roles and responsibilities

Knowing your personal responsibilities under law is vital if you are to play your part in making a site a safe place to work. You should also be aware of your employer's responsibilities, so that you can support them and co-operate with them to create a safe working environment.

Let's look at each of the listed health and safety laws to understand their application on site.

Health and Safety at Work etc. Act (HASAWA) 1974

This legislation applies to all types of workplace and all personnel working in them. This includes those making deliveries to a site, and it also provides protection for those who might be affected by construction activities, such as members of the public who are nearby.

Employer responsibilities under HASAWA

The employer's responsibilities are contained in sections 2 to 9 of the Act. An employer must take care of the health, safety and welfare at work of all its employees. Key areas in which the employer must provide for the employee include:

- a safe working environment with adequate welfare facilities, including safe, secure access and exit
- safe systems of work, including risk assessments and method statements (there is more information on these later in this chapter)
- clear systems for reporting hazards, accidents and near misses
- adequate instruction, training or supervision, including site inductions and tool-box talks
- **personal protective equipment (PPE)** free of charge, ensuring the appropriate PPE is used whenever needed
- facilities for the safe use, handling, storage and transport of components, materials and substances
- any required health and safety information, including health and safety law posters and public liability insurance details.

> **KEY TERM**
>
> **Personal protective equipment (PPE):** all equipment (including clothing affording protection against the weather) which is intended to be worn or held by a person at work and which protects against one or more risks to a person's health or safety

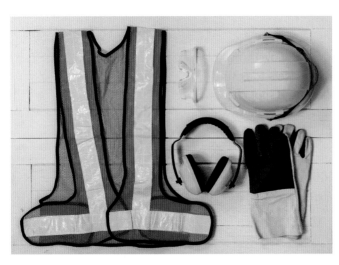

▲ Figure 5.2 PPE must be provided free of charge by the employer

Employee responsibilities under HASAWA

Under HASAWA, your personal responsibilities on site are as follows.

- Always take care and work in a safe manner
- Make sure you do not put yourself or others at risk by your actions or inactions.
- Work in partnership with your employer regarding health and safety.
- Make full use of any equipment and safeguards (for example, PPE) provided by your employer.
- Do not tamper with or alter any safety equipment.
- Report hazards, accidents or near misses in accordance with laws and regulations.

ACTIVITY

Employers are required, by law, to display an HSE-approved health and safety law poster in every workplace (or to provide each worker with the equivalent leaflet). See if you can locate the poster on site or at your training centre.

Reporting of Injuries, Diseases and Dangerous Occurrences Regulations (RIDDOR) 2013

Keeping records of accidents and reporting them to the HSE is governed by RIDDOR 2013. These regulations state that accidents must be reported where they result in an employee or self-employed person being away from work, or unable to perform their normal work duties, for more than seven consecutive days as the result of their injury.

HSE

Health and Safety Executive

Health and Safety at Work etc Act 1974

The Reporting of Injuries, Diseases and Dangerous Occurrence Regulations 1995

F2508 - Report of an injury

Zoom 100 KS i ?

About you and your organisation

*Title *Forename *Family Name

*Job Title *Your Phone No

*Organisation Name

Address Line 1 (eg building name)

Address Line 2 (eg street)

Address Line 3 (eg district)

*Town

County

*Post Code Fax Number

*E-Mail

Remember me ?

*Did the incident happen at the above address? Yes No

*Which authority is responsible fo r monitoring and inspecting health and safety where the incident happened? HSE Local Authority ?

Please refer to the help for guidance on the responsible authority

Next Form Preview

Page 1 of 5

▲ Figure 5.3 An F2508 injury report form

Reproduced by kind permission of HSE. HSE would like to make it clear it has not reviewed this product and does not endorse the business activity of Hodder Education.

ACTIVITY
Visit www.hse.gov.uk and enter 'specified injuries' into the search bar. Choose one of the injuries and write a description of what you think could cause that injury on site.

The HSE website also gives specific details of reportable diseases and dangerous occurrences.

Occupational diseases identified on site must be reported where these are likely to have been caused or made worse by the type of work. Diseases listed on the HSE website include:

- carpal tunnel syndrome
- severe cramp of the hand or forearm
- occupational dermatitis
- hand-arm vibration syndrome
- occupational asthma
- tendonitis or tenosynovitis of the hand or forearm
- any occupational cancer
- any disease attributed to an occupational exposure to a biological agent.

You may not have heard of some of these diseases and injuries. Some of them are discussed later in this chapter. RIDDOR also lists what are termed 'specified injuries' that must be reported.

Dangerous occurrences such as fires, gas leaks and security incidents must be reported. A dangerous occurrence that has not caused an injury (a near miss) should still be reported because if it were to happen again, the consequences may be more serious. Steps can be taken to minimise the likelihood of it being repeated.

Control of Substances Hazardous to Health (COSHH) Regulations 2002 (amended 2004)

The COSHH Regulations 2002 provide guidance on the safe use of potentially dangerous substances, such as acids and chemical products. They also cover hazardous substances produced while working, such as dust generated when cutting or grinding masonry materials.

Hazardous substances already present on a project site may be discovered during the construction process. An example is asbestos, which is also covered by specific regulations (there is more information on this later in the chapter).

Employer responsibilities under COSHH

Key employer responsibilities under COSHH include:

- being familiar with the safety data sheets that are relevant to materials and substances used on the project
- ensuring that known issues with the materials or substances are made known to all personnel
- assessing how operatives could be affected by the materials or substances.

From 2015, the European COSHH symbols were replaced by new international symbols, which are shown in Figure 5.4. You may still come across older stock products that have the European symbol labels on them.

▲ Figure 5.4 COSHH symbols

Employee responsibilities under COSHH

As discussed previously, under HASAWA it is the employer's responsibility to ensure the safe use, handling, storage and transport of components, materials and substances. However, employees must support the employer regarding the safe storage and use of materials and hazardous chemical products on site.

To support the regulations, consideration should be given to substituting hazardous substances with a safer option. For example, water-based paint could be used instead of oil-based paint, or a work method could be changed to reduce the amount of harmful dust or fumes. Always consult with your supervisor if you think that you or others working near you could be affected by hazardous substances being used or produced in the workplace.

Provision and Use of Work Equipment Regulations (PUWER) 1998

These regulations apply to anyone who has responsibility for the safe use of work equipment, such as managers and supervisors. The HSE website states that they apply to '[...] people and companies who own, operate or have control over work equipment. PUWER also places responsibilities on businesses and organisations whose employees use work equipment, whether owned by them or not'.

Under these regulations:

- regular safety inspections of equipment are essential
- work equipment must only be used by workers who have been properly trained to the required level of competence
- relevant information on the safe use of equipment must be provided
- work equipment must only be used for its intended purpose.

ACTIVITY

Visit www.hse.gov.uk/work-equipment-machinery/puwer.htm and look for the section entitled 'What is work equipment' and write your own version of the details given there.

Discuss with another person in your learner group if any workers on site are exempt from applying PUWER.

HEALTH AND SAFETY

Under PUWER, the wheels on a disc cutter used for cutting or grinding can only be changed by someone who has received training to do this. Wrongly fitted wheels can fly apart and cause serious injury.

Manual Handling Operations Regulations 1992 (amended 2002)

Within reason, employers and training providers must arrange for personnel to avoid manual handling if there is a possibility of injury. If manual handling cannot be avoided, then risk assessments must be carried out to establish how to manage and minimise the risk of injury.

Employers need to do everything 'reasonably practicable' to control risk. This means that they must balance the level of risk against the measures needed to control the risk in terms of money, time or trouble.

Employees have general responsibilities under HASAWA to:

- take reasonable care for their own health and safety
- make sure that their activities do not put others at risk
- co-operate with their employer on health and safety matters.

The Manual Handling Operations Regulations supplement these general duties, stating that employees must make 'full and proper use of any system of work provided for their use by their employer'.

Many workplace injuries are a result of incorrect manual handling. Remember that, as well as lifting items, pushing or pulling an object also comes under the Manual Handling Operations Regulations.

Personal Protective Equipment at Work Regulations 1992

Wherever there are risks to health and safety that cannot be adequately controlled in other ways, the Personal Protective Equipment at Work Regulations 1992 require PPE to be supplied as a last resort.

These regulations require that PPE:

- is properly assessed before use to make sure it is fit for purpose
- is maintained and stored properly
- has instructions on how to use it safely
- is used correctly by employees.

All workers on site must make safety an integral part of routine work activities. To support this, you must wear the PPE that your employer provides, look after it while using it and report any damage to it.

Work at Height Regulations 2005 (amended 2007)

These regulations give clear guidance to employers regarding the planning and preparation required for working at height. Employers should put measures in place to keep workers safe and protect them from injury by considering the following points.

- Avoid work at height where it is reasonably possible to do so.
- Where work at height cannot be avoided, minimise the distance and consequences of a fall by using the right type of equipment.

- Do as much work as possible from the ground.
- Make sure that workers can get safely to and from where they work at height.

Training must be provided to make sure that those working at height are informed and competent. All access equipment must be inspected and maintained in accordance with regulations.

There is more on the types and uses of access equipment and working at height later in this chapter.

Control of Noise at Work Regulations 2005

The aim of these regulations is to ensure that workers' hearing is protected from excessive noise at their place of work. Exposure to noise caused by power tools or machinery can cause permanent hearing loss. Damage to hearing can mean a worker loses the ability to understand speech, keep up with conversations or use the telephone.

Employers are required to take action to reduce noise exposure and provide appropriate PPE when noise exceeds specified levels.

Actions to minimise the risk of hearing damage to workers include:

- using quieter equipment or a quieter process
- using isolation screens, barriers and absorbent materials to prevent noise travelling
- improving working techniques to reduce noise levels
- limiting the time that workers spend in noisy areas.

Employers must make sure that workers have appropriate information, instruction and training and must provide appropriate supervision. When working on site, you have the responsibility to make use of any noise-control measures and PPE provided to you.

Control of Vibration at Work Regulations 2005

These regulations cover hand-arm vibration syndrome (HAVS) and whole-body vibration syndrome (WBVS).

- HAVS, also known as 'vibration white finger', is caused by using tools that create a lot of vibration, such as handheld breakers or hammer drills.
- WBVS is caused by the body being shaken or jolted when driving certain types of vehicle or driving over rough and uneven surfaces.

The regulations place a duty on employers to reduce the risk to employees' health from exposure to vibration caused by work activities. It is important to carry out regular risk assessments and put surveillance measures in place.

Exposure to vibration can be limited by carrying out work tasks involving vibration for the shortest time possible.

Electricity at Work Regulations 1989

Electricity is an everyday part of our lives, so it can be easy to take it for granted as an energy source. The Electricity at Work Regulations 1989 require precautions

> **INDUSTRY TIP**
>
> It is good practice to alternate a task involving vibration with other work.

> **ACTIVITY**
>
> Research HAVS on the HSE website and list the symptoms and types of injury that it can cause.

to be taken to prevent the risk of death or personal injury when undertaking work involving electrical equipment.

Under the regulations, employers must ensure that electrical equipment:

- is suitable for its intended purpose
- has been safety-checked before use
- is safely installed and regularly maintained by qualified personnel
- has all its **live** parts protected and inaccessible.

Employees must be adequately trained and informed before working with electrical equipment. Every work activity carried out by employees must be undertaken in such a manner that it does not endanger them or anyone else in the work area.

Remember, any electrical equipment must be used properly, suitable for the work task and maintained in a safe condition. Later in this chapter, we will discuss how this is achieved.

Lifting Operations and Lifting Equipment Regulations (LOLER) 1998

These regulations place duties on people and companies who own, operate or have control over lifting equipment.

'Lifting equipment' includes any work equipment used for lifting or lowering loads, including attachments used for anchoring, fixing or support. The regulations cover a wide range of equipment including cranes, forklift trucks, lifts, hoists, mobile elevated work platforms and vehicle inspection platform hoists. The definition also includes lifting accessories such as chains.

▲ Figure 5.5 Using a scissor lift at height

All operations involving lifting equipment must be:

- properly planned by a competent person
- appropriately supervised
- carried out in a safe manner.

All lifting equipment must be:

- fit for purpose
- appropriate for the task
- suitably marked for record-keeping
- subject to a thorough periodic examination.

Construction, Design and Management (CDM) Regulations 2015

These regulations cover the effective planning and management of a project throughout the life cycle of a building, from conception right through to **demolition**. They require clients, designers and architects to develop the project with safety considerations fully integrated into the design and operational features of the building, to protect construction workers, occupants and those who dismantle the building at the end of its useful life.

> **KEY TERM**
>
> **Demolition:** when something (such as a building) is torn down and destroyed

▲ Figure 5.6 The CDM Regulations play a vital role during demolition

The key requirements under the CDM Regulations can be simplified like this:

- identify hazards and reduce risks
- provide information about the risks that cannot be eliminated
- supply comprehensive information for the health and safety file.

Under the CDM Regulations, the HSE must be notified about certain projects before they start. A duty holder must be appointed, who is trained, competent and experienced enough to know how to avoid specific dangers. The level of competence will differ depending on the type of work, and there may be a number of duty holders.

2 HEALTH AND WELFARE CONSIDERATIONS FOR WORKING ON SITE

Everyone on site must work hard to create a safe working environment. Accidents do not just affect the person who has the accident. Work colleagues or members of the public might be affected, and so will the employer. On site, be observant at all times and carefully consider the safety of those working near you.

2.1 Accidents and injuries at work

A construction site has many hazards and potential hazards that must be removed or suitably managed through well-designed risk assessments and method statements (more on these later in this chapter). These health and safety documents are only effective if all personnel on site use them appropriately.

Large building sites may have a safety officer permanently on site. Smaller sites may have safety officers who visit regularly. These officials are responsible for:

- promoting health and safety awareness
- providing information to employers, employees and others who may be affected by work activities.

Listen to their advice and do not be afraid to ask questions about safety matters. They are trained personnel who support the implementation of HSE guidance on strategies to prevent accidents and injuries occurring in the workplace.

Some of the potential consequences of accidents that can have an effect on all site workers are:

- emotional trauma
- loss of production
- poor company image
- increased insurance costs
- closure of the site.

ACTIVITY

Look at the list of potential consequences of an accident. Think of some other personal consequences that could be added to the list.

Table 5.1 gives details of common hazards that must be managed on site.

▼ Table 5.1 Types of hazards

Type of hazard	How it can be caused	How it can be prevented
Slips, trips and falls ▲ Loose brick bands can be a trip hazard	• Trailing cables • Discarded brick or block pallet bands • Partially buried obstructions • Discarded waste materials • Unprotected excavations	• Maintain good housekeeping. • Be observant and watch where you are walking. • Take action to remove trip hazards.
Manual handling injuries ▲ Incorrect manual handling can cause injuries	• Incorrect lifting techniques • Awkward-shaped loads • Obstructions in the path of travel when moving items	• Use correct lifting techniques. • Get assistance to move awkward loads. • Plan the movement of items to make sure the path of travel is clear.
Electrocution ▲ Cables can be damaged easily	• Electrical items immersed in water • Damaged cables • Using poorly maintained or damaged equipment	• Keep electrical items and cables dry. • Inspect power tools and equipment for damage before use. • Take damaged equipment out of service and inform your supervisor about the fault.
Injuries from fires ▲ Store flammable liquids correctly	• Unauthorised burning of waste • Misuse of flammable liquids • Poor storage of flammable items	• Do not light fires on site. • Handle and store flammable liquids correctly.

▼ Table 5.1 Types of hazards (continued)

Type of hazard	How it can be caused	How it can be prevented
Hand-arm vibration syndrome (HAVS, also known as vibration white finger) ▲ HAVS	• Using tools that create a lot of vibration, such as handheld breakers or hammer drills	• Avoid using tools that cause vibration for long periods. • Alternate the task involving vibration with other work. • Always use the right tool for the job and make sure cutting edges are sharp to make the tool as efficient as possible.

Building sites can be noisy, dusty places and can require you to work in potentially hazardous situations. Protect yourself and others from injury by being aware of these additional areas of concern.

- Use appropriate PPE. Even relatively minor injuries like cuts and splinters can develop into more serious problems if they become infected. Wearing gloves is a simple precaution.
- As mentioned previously, noise can damage your hearing permanently. Use the correct PPE and take steps to reduce your exposure to prolonged noise.
- Dust and fumes can cause long-term or even permanent damage to your lungs and airways (respiratory problems). Use the correct PPE and monitor your surroundings for activities that cause excess dust or damaging fumes. If the problem is temporary, move away. If the problem is ongoing, speak to your supervisor about preventing the problem.
- Skin contact with some substances, such as cement dust or oil, can cause conditions like dermatitis, which causes itchy, dry skin or a rash on swollen, reddened skin. Wear gloves or use a barrier cream to protect your skin. Wash and dry your hands thoroughly after work.
- Repetitive movement during work tasks can cause repetitive strain injury (RSI). This can result in muscle pain and over long periods can even affect your bones. Take regular breaks from repetitive work. Do some stretching exercises and keep warm during cold weather when working outdoors.
- Working at height requires careful observation and movement around the elevated work platform. Falls from height are still the major cause of death on construction sites, despite the formulation of comprehensive laws and regulations to protect workers. Even falling from a relatively low height (such as standing on a chair) can cause serious injury and broken bones.

2.2 Reporting procedures

When there are ten or more workers on site, records about accidents must be kept in an accident book to comply with regulations. This is true even if there is no need to report the accident to the HSE.

By making reports and keeping records of accidents on site, it is possible to see patterns that may be emerging, possibly due to bad habits or incorrect work practices. These records can assist in planning future work activities to reduce the occurrence of accidents and may be used when legal matters arise relating to an accident or emergency.

The accident book confirms all the details of an accident occurring on site, including:

- the date and time of the accident
- who was injured
- the nature of the injuries
- how the accident happened.

Details are entered into the accident book, by the injured person if possible, and the entry should be checked for accuracy by a qualified first-aider. If the injured worker is unable to make the entry, another person can do it for them. The information recorded may include witness details, and all information must be kept confidential.

Individual organisations and companies may have their own health and safety recording documentation, which you will need to get familiar with. For example, on-site records can be used to provide information about personnel trained to give first aid.

First aid is designed to stabilise a patient for later treatment if required, so proper training of first-aiders is vital. The injured person may be taken to hospital by ambulance and other emergency services may need to be called. The first-aider must be able to communicate effectively with supervisors and safety officers who are authorised site personnel.

INDUSTRY TIP

Even minor injuries like a cut finger or a splinter from wood should be recorded in an accident book on site. Do not be tempted to think 'it will be all right'. If the cut were to get infected later on, having a record of when the original injury occurred could be useful.

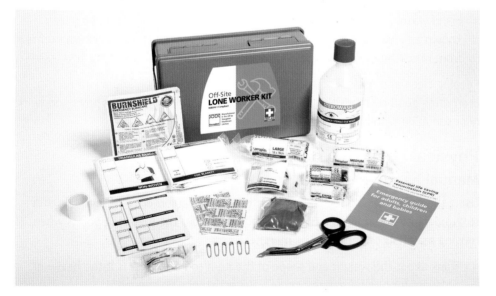

▲ Figure 5.7 A first-aid kit

ACTIVITY

Locate the first-aid kit where you work or train. Make a list of the items it contains and check online that it conforms to basic requirements.

If you are near an accident or emergency situation on site, make the area safe, if it does not put you in danger to do so, and get help. If necessary, call for a first-aider. Make sure that you or someone else calls the emergency services and reports the matter immediately to your supervisor. Your supervisor will alert the site safety officer, who will assess the situation carefully.

2.3 Personal welfare

Personal hygiene

An important welfare consideration when working with others is personal cleanliness and hygiene. The control of transmissible diseases protects both workers on site and the wider community.

Something as simple as regular hand washing is an important part of maintaining good personal hygiene.

- Many construction activities involve exposure to contamination from soil and from a range of substances within materials that can cause illness. An example is operatives who work with lead, a soft metal that invites being shaped by hand. While this material is not dangerous when touched or in contact with the skin, it is a hazard if ingested (swallowed). Invisible particles of lead on your hands must be washed off after working with the metal, and this is especially important before eating.
- Other substances such as cement dust should be washed off as soon as possible and hands should be washed thoroughly at the end of the working day to minimise the risk of skin irritation and diseases. If your clothing becomes contaminated, change into clean clothing and wash your hands and face before eating.
- Hand washing will also protect against diseases such as leptospirosis (also known as Weil's disease). This is a serious disease spread by contact with urine from rats, which are often present on construction sites.

Keeping clean and maintaining personal hygiene also plays an important part in promoting good relationships between workers. No one appreciates having to work near someone who has not washed.

Physical health

Manual handling

Using the correct lifting techniques and the proper equipment is essential in order to avoid injury and maintain physical health. Consider the following points when moving materials or components manually.

- Think about the weight and shape of the item to be moved. Is it too heavy or awkward for one person to handle? Will assistance be needed?
- Is there a lifting aid or a mechanical means of moving the load?
- Make sure the path along which the load is to be moved is clear of obstructions.
- Avoid twisting your body or reaching too much when moving the load.

For safety and efficiency, most sites have some means of moving heavy items mechanically, such as a forklift or crane. If items cannot be moved by mechanical means and must be moved manually, methods have been developed to move and handle components and materials efficiently and in a way that reduces the risk of injury. One recommended method is called **kinetic** lifting.

KEY TERM

Kinetic: relating to, caused by or producing movement

▲ Figure 5.8 Safe kinetic lifting technique

To employ the kinetic lifting method shown in Figure 5.8, keep the following points in mind.

- Always lift with your back straight.
- Keep your elbows in, your knees bent and your feet slightly apart.
- When placing the item, be sure to use the leg muscles, bending your knees.
- Beware of trapping your fingers when stacking materials.
- Place the item on levelled, carefully spaced bearers if required.

For very heavy items, get assistance from one or more helpers. Assign one person in the team to be in charge and make sure that lifting is done in a co-operative way.

INDUSTRY TIP

An item may not be too heavy for one person to lift, but it may be awkward to move on your own without causing injury, perhaps to others nearby. For example, a long length of timber should be moved with one person at each end to avoid causing injury to others on site.

Noise

A single loud noise or persistent lower levels of noise can cause damage to your hearing that cannot be repaired. An indication of when you should wear ear defenders or use ear plugs is when you have to raise your voice to carry out a normal conversation two metres apart from someone.

Hearing loss caused by noisy work conditions may severely impact on quality of life, with adverse effects on social, functional and psychological well-being. For example, in-person and telephone conversations become difficult, with confusion of similar words leading to misunderstandings.

ACTIVITY

Visit www.hse.gov.uk/noise/video/hearingvideo.htm and watch 'The Hearing Video' to see how important it is to protect your hearing.

HEALTH AND SAFETY

Research tinnitus online to find out the symptoms and what causes it. Is there a cure?

▲ Figure 5.9 Ear defenders

▲ Figure 5.10 Ear plugs

There is a legal duty for manufacturers and suppliers to provide information on the levels of noise their equipment produces. Understanding this information can help establish the precautions required to protect users from noise-related injury. Ask your supervisor for assistance if the information is not clear. Where possible, choose low-noise tools and equipment.

Poor maintenance of tools can lead to increases in noise levels. Make sure that the tools or equipment you are using are properly maintained and that any noise-suppression devices are fitted and working.

Vibration

Injuries caused by prolonged exposure to vibration can be painful, disabling and irreversible. Hand-arm vibration syndrome (HAVS) affects blood vessels, nerves and joints in the fingers, hands and arms. It can cause permanent damage, preventing a worker from carrying out many normal day-to-day activities.

Over time, parts of the fingers go white and numb, which has led to the condition being referred to as 'vibration white finger', and there can also be a loss of touch and sensitivity. The greater the exposure to vibration, the more likely there is to be damage.

Workers can protect themselves from vibration damage in several ways.

- Limit the time you use **percussion tools** such as breakers and drills. Take regular breaks.
- Avoid gripping the tool tightly. A tight grip will transmit more vibration.
- Avoid forcing the tool into the work piece to speed the job up. This will simply add to vibrations experienced by the operator. Let the tool do the work.
- Make it a common practice to alternate jobs exposing you to vibration with other tasks that are vibration-free.
- Always use the right tool for the job and ensure that cutting edges are sharp to make the tool as efficient as possible.
- Keep warm and dry to encourage good blood circulation, and massage your fingers during breaks from work.

Mental health

Mental health is about how we think and feel. Poor mental health can become obvious in our behaviour, potentially leading to relationship difficulties in the workplace.

Anxiety and depression are common mental-health problems that are often a reaction to stress. By taking action to remove or reduce stress in the workplace, employers can help to prevent people becoming ill and assist those with existing illness to manage it.

There is often pressure in the workplace to meet deadlines, but there is a clear distinction between pressure, which can be a motivating force, and stress, which occurs when this pressure becomes excessive.

In 2019, the HSE produced a workbook on tackling work-related stress. It proposed what is referred to as the 'Management Standards approach', which identifies six key areas of work design that, if not properly managed, can contribute to stress at work:

- demands – workload, work patterns and work environment
- control – a worker's influence over the way they work
- support – encouragement, sponsorship and resources provided by an organisation, managers and fellow workers
- relationships – promoting positive working to avoid conflict and dealing with unacceptable behaviour
- role – a worker's understanding of where they 'fit in'
- change – the way changes on site are managed and communicated.

Making an analysis of a worker's conditions based on these factors is part of the legal duties of an employer to care for the mental health of employees.

As an employee, you can take care of your own mental health by being open about problems and stresses that affect you. Responsible employers must make provision for their workers to communicate their concerns through a number of formal and informal channels, such as:

- supervisors or managers
- trades union representatives
- health and safety representatives
- human resources personnel
- occupational health advisors.

You could also make use of counselling services or consult your GP.

Mental health can be protected and illness can be prevented if action is taken early to address stress-related problems. Think about it: if you broke a bone in your arm, you would not hesitate to get help. Take the same approach with mental health – get help when it is needed. You should find out about the facilities a company has in place to assist workers and whom to approach if you want support.

ACTIVITY

From time to time, everyone has to deal with stresses in life, such as taking exams. Think about a stressful situation you have faced. Write down how you coped and discuss your thoughts with someone else from your learner group.

A known cause of stress on site is bullying. This can take the form of physical attacks, verbal harassment and exclusion from social groups. No one should have their confidence and well-being undermined by a bully. A victim of bullying can take action to deal with the situation, which will be of benefit to all workers on site, by:

- consulting your company's bullying policy
- speaking to someone you feel comfortable with
- following your company's complaints procedure to tackle the matter.

Substance abuse

Workers on site have a responsibility to look after the safety and welfare of themselves and others by acting appropriately regarding the use of alcohol and drugs during working hours.

There is zero tolerance for the use and abuse of alcohol and drugs on site. Alcohol and drugs can have a serious effect on your performance and behaviour in the workplace, reducing your perception of risk, causing a loss of concentration and impairing your balance. Remaining on a construction site under the influence of alcohol or drugs is dangerous, and a worker in that condition will be excluded from the site and could face serious consequences. Remember that alcohol or drugs used in your own time can still have an effect many hours later, potentially during working hours.

Keep in mind also that some medication can affect a worker in an undesirable way under certain circumstances.

Put the health, safety and welfare of yourself and others working near you at the forefront of everything you plan for and work towards on site.

2.4 Site welfare

The welfare of workers on site is protected individually and collectively by regulations that focus on the effective planning and management of construction projects, with health and safety considerations to the fore.

Table 5.2 gives details of welfare facilities required by the CDM Regulations 2015.

▼ Table 5.2 Welfare facilities that must be provided by employers

Facility	Regulation requirement
Clean drinking water	Clean drinking water must be provided or made available. There should be appropriate signs showing where drinking water is available. Unless the supply of drinking water is from a water fountain, cups should be provided.
Toilets	Enough suitable toilets should be provided or made available. Toilets should be: • adequately ventilated and lit • maintained in a clean condition • separate for male and female employees.

▼ Table 5.2 Welfare facilities that must be provided by employers (continued)

Facility	Regulation requirement
Washing facilities	Enough washing facilities must be available and include showers if required by the nature of the work. They should be: ● in the same place as the toilets and near any changing rooms ● supplied with clean hot (or warm) and cold running water, soap and towels ● separate for male and female employees, unless the area is for washing the hands and face only.
Changing rooms and lockers	If operatives must wear special clothing and if they cannot be expected to change elsewhere, changing rooms must be provided or made available. Separate rooms for male and female employees should be available where necessary. There should be facilities for operatives to dry clothing, with seating where necessary. Lockers should be provided.
Canteens, rest rooms or rest areas	There should be enough tables and seating with backrests for the number of operatives using them at any one time, as well as facilities for preparing, heating and eating food. There must be provision to boil water.

ACTIVITY

Look around your workplace or training centre. Make a list of the welfare facilities available where you work or train and note how they compare to the regulation requirements in Table 5.2.

③ UNDERSTANDING THE PRINCIPLES OF RISK MANAGEMENT

The occurrence of accidents and emergencies can be minimised and often prevented by assessing and managing the risks involved in performing a work task in defined conditions. To comply with HASAWA, employers must establish ongoing processes to deal with the changing conditions on site as a project develops.

3.1 Terminology

▼ Table 5.3 Key terminology for understanding risk management

Accident	An accident can be defined as an unforeseen and unplanned event. On a construction site, an accident can have serious consequences involving harm, injury, damage or loss. To be classified as an accident, there must be an identifiable external event that results in clear consequences.
Near miss	A near miss is an event that does not cause harm, but has the potential to cause injury, ill health or death. An example could be a loaded pallet falling to the ground from a forklift as it is being transported across site. Workers nearby may be unharmed, but if the falling load had hit workers, the consequences would have been serious.
Hazard	A hazard can be defined as a situation, an object or a behaviour that could cause harm, whether that is injury or illness to personnel or damage in the work environment. Some classifications and examples of hazards are: ● physical, for example, extreme temperature or excessive noise ● mechanical, for example, unguarded moving parts of machinery ● chemical, for example, fumes causing breathing problems or acids causing skin irritations.
Risk	Risk can be defined as the likelihood of a hazard causing harm. The level of risk is calculated by multiplying the likelihood of the hazard causing harm by the potential severity of that harm.
Competence	In the context of risk management, the HSE defines competence as 'the combination of training, skills, experience and knowledge that a person has, and their ability to apply them to perform a task safely'. An employer will consider the competence of relevant workers when carrying out a risk assessment.

3.2 Risk assessment process

Purpose of completing a risk assessment

Managing hazards in the workplace is essential if accidents and injuries are to be avoided. The main tool used to do this is a document known as a risk assessment. It is created either by the employer or by a self-employed consultant.

A risk assessment can be split into the following three key stages.

1 Identify hazards and potential hazards in the workplace.
2 Evaluate the risks caused by these hazards.
3 Establish control measures to remove or reduce risks.

The findings should be recorded, and the effectiveness of the assessment should be reviewed periodically. A review should take place when work patterns or task details change to make sure that hazards are continuously managed and controlled.

> **ACTIVITY**
>
> Choose a trade you are familiar with (for example, carpentry) and a related work activity (such as cutting roof timbers). Use an online risk assessment template to assess the work activity you have selected.

Hazard identification

To identify actual and potential hazards, an examination of the workplace and work practices must take place. Key factors that must be considered include:

- regular patterns of work
- the way tools and equipment are used
- levels of safety in current work practices
- the condition of the work premises.

It can be useful to look back at past accident records and details of illness among workers to identify obvious hazards. Many hazards to health should be relatively easy to identify, such as injury due to poor manual handling techniques, careless handling or storage of chemicals and work-related stress. Consideration should also be given to non-routine activities, maintenance work and cleaning operations.

Risk ratings and control measures

Once hazards and potential hazards have been identified, the level of risk must be established by deciding:

- the likelihood that a hazard will cause harm (rated from most unlikely to most likely)
- the possible severity of that harm (rated from trivial to major).

> **INDUSTRY TIP**
>
> You can find more information on managing risk on the HSE website: www.hse.gov.uk/simple-health-safety/risk

Numerical values are then given to the assessment of likelihood and severity. To establish the risk rating, you need to multiply these two figures together. Study Figure 5.11 to see how this works.

		Severity			
		1 Trivial injury	2 Slight injury	3 Serious injury	4 Major injury
Likelihood	1 Most unlikely	1	2	3	4
	2 Unlikely	2	4	6	8
	3 Likely	3	6	9	12
	4 Most likely	4	8	12	16

Assessed band	Control measures
1 or 2 Minimal risk	Maintain existing control measures
3 or 4 Low risk	Review existing control measures
6 or 8 Medium risk	Improve existing control measures
9, 12 or 16 High risk	Stop work until the risk is reduced

▲ Figure 5.11 Risk ratings and control measures

Permits to work and method statements

A specific control document called a permit to work can be used for work situations where there is a risk of accidents leading to major injury, such as maintenance activities where personnel must work inside or close to heavy machinery. It authorises certain people to carry out specific work tasks within a given timeframe and sets out the precautions needed to complete the work safely.

Method statements can form part of a permit to work and are used alongside risk assessments. They give a clear uncomplicated sequence of work to complete the specified task and can be used to record the specific hazards and potential hazards associated with the task. An employer will have a method statement written for all trade tasks that will be performed during a project.

Make sure that you consult risk assessments and method statements before you start work on your assigned tasks.

3.3 Personal protective equipment

Employers must provide appropriate PPE without charge to employees, including agency workers where they are legally recognised as employed by the contractor.

If PPE is not cared for properly and stored correctly, it can be damaged and may not provide adequate protection to the user. For example, ultraviolet light from the sun will cause the plastic that a hard hat is made from to deteriorate over time. Some pens and paints that might be used to write on a hard hat can also damage the plastic.

Check the condition and date of manufacture of every piece of PPE you use and get a replacement if it is damaged or out of date.

Table 5.4 shows the types of PPE used in the workplace.

▼ Table 5.4 Types of PPE used in the workplace

PPE	Uses
Hard hats/safety helmets	Hard hats must be worn when there is danger of: ● striking your head on overhead obstructions ● being hit by objects falling from above. Most sites insist on hard hats being worn at all times. They must be adjusted to fit your head correctly and must not be worn back to front.
Steel-toe cap boots or shoes	Steel-toe cap boots or shoes are worn at all times on site to protect the feet from crushing by heavy objects. Some safety footwear has additional insole protection to help prevent nails going up through the foot.
Ear defenders and ear plugs	Your hearing can be permanently damaged by a single loud noise or even persistent lower noise levels. Hearing protection in the form of ear defenders or ear plugs is an important item of PPE.

▼ Table 5.4 Types of PPE used in the workplace (continued)

PPE	Uses
High-visibility (hi-vis) jackets 	High-visibility clothing is essential on site, so that other people can see you easily. Plant or machinery working nearby or moving around a site is a potential danger to all workers.
Goggles and safety glasses 	Dust and flying debris are a constant feature of a construction site. Your eyes can be easily damaged. Wearing goggles or safety glasses is a simple way to protect them.
Dust masks and respirators 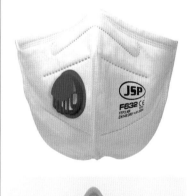	Dust can damage your lungs and cause serious illnesses that can be life-threatening. A dust mask gives vital protection when correctly fitted. A respirator is used to filter out hazardous gases. Respirators are rated P1, P2 and P3 to show the level of protection they provide. Equipment that protects your breathing is referred to as RPE (respiratory protective equipment).

▼ Table 5.4 Types of PPE used in the workplace (continued)

PPE	Uses
Knee pads 	Knee pads are essential protection for the knee joints when kneeling for extended periods.
Gloves	Gloves protect against cuts, abrasions, skin irritations, chemical burns and splinters. A range of gloves are available to suit different work tasks, providing a good grip and protecting the fingers.
Safety harnesses	When working at height, fall-arrest systems must be used where a working platform is not enclosed or lacks safeguards such as hand rails. A safety harness is often used when scaffolding is being erected and is not yet complete.

INDUSTRY TIP

Waterproof clothing and overalls can also be used as protection in extreme working conditions.

ACTIVITY

Find a supplier of PPE online and make a note of how much each item of PPE in Table 5.4 costs (there is no need to do extensive research – just use the cost of the first item you come across in each instance). Add up the total cost for a full set of items.

Think about the cost to your employer if it must provide PPE for each worker on site. Look after your PPE – it is a valuable provision!

SITE SAFETY

Hard hat must be worn

Protective footwear must be worn

High visibility jackets must be worn

Ear protectors must be worn

Warning
Construction site

Keep out

Danger
Demolition work in progress

No admittance for unauthorised personnel

Site safety starts here

▲ Figure 5.12 A site safety sign showing the PPE required to work in this area

3.4 Emergency procedures

People often panic in an emergency situation. Every worker on site should be prepared in case an emergency occurs. Being prepared will give you the confidence to act calmly and assist others.

You should know where the fire assembly point is in advance of a possible evacuation. If you are not at the fire assembly point when an alarm is sounding and other people have to look for you, they could be put at risk.

▲ Figure 5.13 Fire assembly points will be marked with signs

INDUSTRY TIP

Familiarise yourself with fire escape routes and alarm signals on site, especially if you are a new starter.

If you discover an emergency situation, such as a fire, explosion or security incident, raise the alarm immediately.

If an alarm sounds:

- calmly but quickly proceed to the designated assembly point
- follow signs showing evacuation routes on site
- do not take any belongings with you while moving to the assembly point
- do not return to your work location until the appointed person states it is safe to do so.

Fire safety

Fire safety relies on all personnel on site or in a training centre being aware of the potential hazards that could lead to an outbreak of fire.

For a fire to exist, three things are needed:

- oxygen – a gas that occurs naturally in the air
- heat – such as a spark or naked flame
- fuel – any material or substance that is combustible.

If all three of these things are present, a fire is unavoidable. If one of these things is missing, a fire cannot occur. This is often referred to as the 'fire triangle'.

▲ Figure 5.14 The fire triangle

Maintaining a clean and tidy workplace is a key factor in helping to prevent fires from starting and spreading.

In order to contribute to fire safety, you need to know the location of fire extinguishers and fire blankets in your workplace or training centre and which type can be used on different fires.

Fires are classified according to the type of fuel that is burning. Study Table 5.5 to see which extinguishers can be used for each type of fire.

▼ Table 5.5 Fire classifications and extinguishers

Classification of fire	Type of fuel	Type of extinguisher to use
A	Wood, paper, hair, textiles	Water, foam, dry powder
B	Flammable liquids	Foam, dry powder, CO_2
C	Flammable gases	Dry powder, CO_2
D	Flammable metals	Specially formulated dry powder
Electrical	–	CO_2, dry powder
F	Cooking oils	Fire blanket

An additional type of fire extinguisher called a P50 is certified to deal with a wide range of fire classifications.

It is important to use the correct extinguisher to deal with the different types of fire, as using the wrong one could make the danger much worse. For example, using a water extinguisher on an electrical fire could lead to the user being electrocuted. Although all fire extinguishers are red, they each have a different coloured label to identify their contents, as shown in Table 5.6.

▼ Table 5.6 Types of fire extinguisher

Type	Label colour	Image
Water	Red	
Foam	Cream	
Carbon dioxide (CO_2)	Black	
Dry powder	Blue	

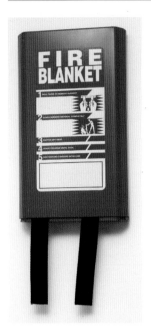

▲ Figure 5.15 Fire blanket

Fire blankets are designed to extinguish small fires before they spread. They consist of a sheet of fire-retardant material that is placed over a fire in order to smother it.

3.5 Safety signs and notices

Safety signs and notices in the workplace can help to manage potential hazards and reduce accidents and emergencies.

You should be familiar with a range of standardised safety signs used in construction. Look at Table 5.7 to see some examples.

▼ Table 5.7 Safety signs and notices

Type of sign	Description
Prohibition	A circle with a red outline and a red line from the top left to the bottom right Tells you that something *must not* be done
Mandatory	A circle with a blue background and white symbol or text Tells you that something must be done
Caution	A yellow triangle with a black outline Warns you of danger

ACTIVITY

Look for prohibition and mandatory signs in your workplace or training centre. List two different applications for each type of sign. (Hint: a common prohibition sign is 'No smoking'.)

▼ Table 5.7 Safety signs and notices (continued)

Type of sign	Description
Safe condition 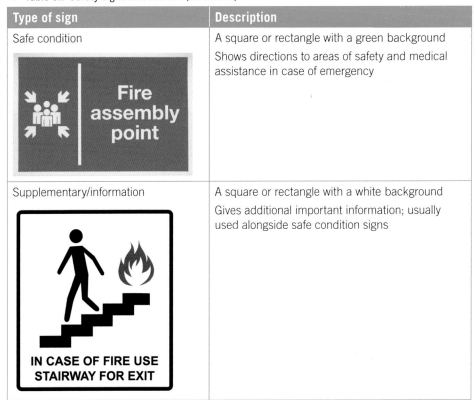	A square or rectangle with a green background Shows directions to areas of safety and medical assistance in case of emergency
Supplementary/information	A square or rectangle with a white background Gives additional important information; usually used alongside safe condition signs

④ EQUIPMENT AND ASSOCIATED RISKS

4.1 Access equipment and working at height

As mentioned previously, falls from height are one of the biggest causes of fatalities and major injuries on UK construction sites. 'Working at height' takes place in any place where, if there were no precautions in place, a person could fall a distance liable to cause personal injury.

Employing safe methods of work and using suitable access equipment correctly are vital factors in keeping yourself and others safe when working at height. Experienced workers should assist inexperienced workers to keep safe – do not be afraid to speak to others plainly about something you think might be unsafe.

If work at height is necessary, think about these points before you start work.

- Make sure that the equipment selected is suitable for the job. Using the incorrect equipment can lead to disaster.
- Make sure that the equipment is stable and strong enough for the job and has been maintained and inspected regularly, especially after bad weather. If there are broken, damaged or missing components, do not use it. All equipment should be checked for safe condition before use and inspection tags and notices should be up to date. Never take short cuts!
- Remember, whatever type of elevated platform you use, keep the deck of the platform free of loose materials and waste. Slips or trips at height could lead to a fall, which could result in severe injury or death.
- Be responsible and provide protection for people below you from falling objects. Make sure there are barriers to prevent materials falling from the working platform and keep your work area tidy.
- Finally, after use, make sure that all equipment is stored properly. Ladders should be stored undercover on a flat surface or hung on brackets positioned at regular intervals. Scaffold tubes should be stacked neatly in racks and scaffold boards should be stacked on top of each other on level-spaced bearers raised above the floor. Keep all access equipment in clean condition and lubricate moving parts regularly.

A risk assessment and method statement must be produced by competent personnel before work at height begins. These documents will assist in choosing the right type of access equipment. There are various types of access equipment suitable for a range of specific jobs.

We will now look at how the Work at Height Regulations 2005 (amended 2007) are designed to protect you when using some specific types of equipment.

Ladders

Ladders are mainly used for access onto an elevated working platform, but the regulations allow for their use as a working platform for light work over short periods. The top of the ladder must be secured against something firm and stable, not something flexible such as plastic guttering.

Strong upper resting point

Adequate lap on extension ladders

Ground back slope not exceeding 6°

Ground side slope not exceeding 16°, clean and free of slippery algae and moss

▲ Figure 5.16 Using a ladder correctly

▲ Figure 5.17 Resting ladders on plastic guttering can cause it to bend and break

IMPROVE YOUR ENGLISH

Visit www.hse.gov.uk and search for 'safe use of ladders and stepladders'.

In your own words, write a summary of the guidance about when you can use a ladder as a working platform.

A ladder should be set at an angle of 75° to the ground. Using a ratio of 1:4 ensures that you are placing your ladder at the correct angle; the distance between the wall and the base of the ladder should be one-quarter of the ladder's height.

INDUSTRY TIPS

Take your time and be observant when setting up a ladder. Many workers have rushed to get on with a job and fallen because they failed to notice a problem until it was too late.

Some ladders have markings on their side to assist in establishing the correct angle.

There are ladders designed for specific purposes, such as accessing a roof surface without causing damage to it. Always use a ladder that is designed for the job.

Some ladders are fixed in length (pole ladders) and others can be extended (extension ladders). When using an extension ladder, make sure that sufficient overlap is left between the two sections to maintain the strength and stability of the whole unit.

▲ Figure 5.18 Roof ladder

Stepladders

Stepladders are designed for short-term light work when used as a working platform.

Be careful not to reach out too far from the side of the stepladder because this could cause it to topple sideways.

If the stepladder has a shelf at the top, do not use this as a step. This is designed to carry light loads, such as tins of paint, or as a rest for placing small tools.

Always check ladders and stepladders carefully before using them. Check the stiles (uprights) and rungs (steps) for damage such as splits or cracks.

INDUSTRY TIP

Do not use painted ladders or stepladders because the paint could be hiding damage.

Working from the side can make stepladders unstable, so do not overreach

Don't stand on the top three steps

Stepladder is fully open

Locked open firm and level on the ground

▲ Figure 5.19 Using a stepladder correctly

▼ Table 5.8 Using ladders and stepladders safely

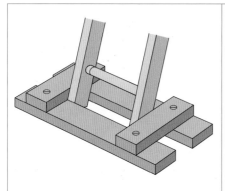

Properly secure ladders at the base

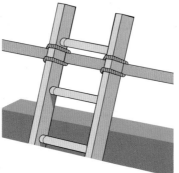

Properly secure ladders at the top

Extend the ladder 1 m above the landing point to give you something hold onto

Use the top of the stepladder as a shelf, not as a step

Do not overreach to the side and do not change rungs during a work task

Keep at least three points of contact with the ladder – both your feet and one hand

INDUSTRY TIP

Trestles are best used on a smooth level floor. If you have to set them up on an uneven surface, take extra care to make sure that they are stable before starting work.

Trestles

Trestles form an access system used for relatively short durations. They are not designed to carry heavy loadings, so users should limit the weight placed on the platform when stacking materials for a work task.

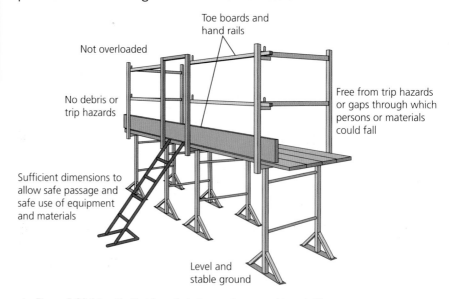

▲ Figure 5.20 A trestle that is safe to be used as a working platform

Mobile tower scaffold

Mobile tower scaffolds are manufactured from galvanised steel or lightweight aluminium alloy. They must be assembled by competent operatives in accordance with the manufacturer's instructions.

They should always have guard rails and toe boards fitted when in use, to prevent you and the materials you are using from accidentally falling from the working platform.

Pay attention to these important points when using a mobile tower scaffold.

- Read and follow the manufacturer's instructions.
- Use the equipment for its intended purpose.
- Do not exceed the maximum height given in the manufacturer's instructions.
- Do not overload the working platform.
- Make sure the wheels of the scaffold are on a firm surface (some scaffolds have feet instead of wheels).
- Unload the working platform and, if necessary, reduce the height before moving the scaffold.
- Do not move a tower scaffold if workers are standing on it.

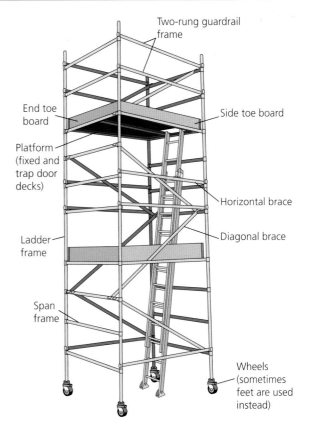

▲ Figure 5.21 A tower scaffold and its parts

Fixed scaffold

Fixed tubular scaffold is erected by specialist scaffolding companies who employ trained and highly competent operatives. It is assembled using steel tubes and clips, (referred to as 'fittings'), which bolt together tightly in a specified pattern.

Some types of tubular scaffold are designed to be assembled using specially shaped cups on the upright tubes, which allow horizontal tubing to be slotted into them and wedged together tightly. This is sometimes referred to as 'system scaffolding'.

▲ Figure 5.22 Safe scaffold being set up

Never alter tubular scaffold yourself. There can be a temptation to remove hand rails to allow materials to be placed more conveniently on the working platform by forklift or crane. However, to do so would be dangerous to yourself and others working on the scaffold.

When stacking materials on tubular scaffold, make sure that the load is spread evenly to distribute the weight carried by the structure.

INDUSTRY TIP

Scaffold is inspected by qualified personnel at regular intervals and a tag is attached to show the inspection date.

Even if the scaffold has recently been inspected and passed as safe, always be observant and alert to the possibility that someone has made an unauthorised change to the equipment after the inspection, so something could be loose or missing. When working at height, be attentive!

Tubular scaffold has been in use for many years, with refinements in its design to improve safety. Two types of tubular scaffold have been used:

- independent tubular scaffold, which transmits the loadings carried by it to the ground
- putlog tubular scaffold (which is not often used now), which transmits the loadings partly to the ground and partly to the building under construction.

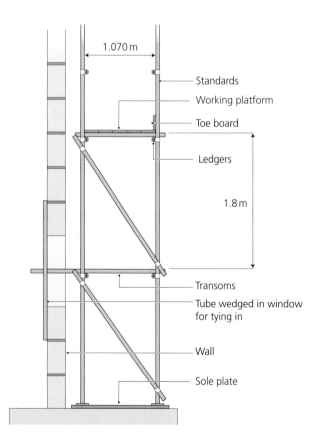

▲ Figure 5.23 Independent tubular scaffold

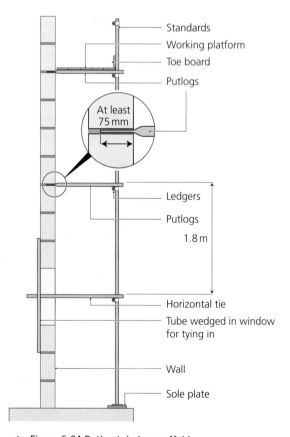

▲ Figure 5.24 Putlog tubular scaffold

Scaffolding must be erected and used so that it satisfies the following requirements.

- Hand rails, guards, toe boards and working platforms must have no gaps along their length.
- Systems and equipment for lifting materials to the level of the working platform must comply with safety regulations.
- Systems and equipment for removing waste and debris from the elevated working platform must be safe. Never throw waste materials off the working platform of a scaffold. Use a debris chute or place the materials securely on a pallet or in a container for controlled removal by forklift or crane.

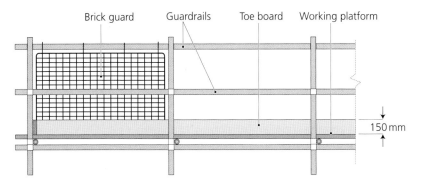

▲ Figure 5.25 Elements of a safe working platform

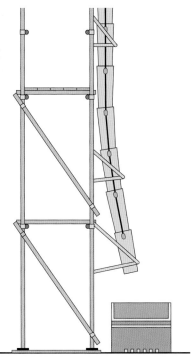

▲ Figure 5.26 A debris chute attached to scaffolding

Mobile elevated work platform (MEWP)

A MEWP is designed to allow one or more workers to access work at height safely. Sometimes, you may hear it referred to as a 'cherry picker'. When operated correctly, it can allow fast access to difficult locations in a safe manner.

A MEWP is not a crane and should not be used to lift heavy loads. (There is more information on lifting equipment in section 4.3.) Never operate a MEWP unless you are trained and competent.

4.2 Power tools

Tools may be powered by mains electricity, batteries, compressed air or fuel such as petrol.

Powered equipment can cause serious injury, since it often has rapidly moving or rotating parts. Do not wear loose-fitting clothing that could become entangled in the machinery. Treat power tools with respect.

Never use a tool for a job it is not designed for. For example, an impact screwdriver is not a drill and should not be used as one.

After use, store cleaned portable power tools and equipment in carrying boxes in a clean and secure location, making sure that all the parts and accessories are present and undamaged. Cables should be inspected before being wound onto reels or neatly coiled to avoid them becoming tangled or damaged.

ACTIVITY

Visit www.youtube.com/watch?v=veF4uSUtrEY to watch the 'Scaffolding Training Video' by Sprout Labs.

This video shows how trained scaffolders reduce the risks associated with working at height.

▲ Figure 5.27 A cherry picker can provide a safe working platform

Mains electricity-powered tools

It should never be forgotten that electricity can be dangerous if it is not treated with respect, with the potential to cause severe injury or even death. Make sure that you are properly trained before using electrical equipment in the workplace. Never dismantle or adjust electrical equipment of any kind. Leave it to someone who is authorised, trained and competent.

When working with or near equipment powered by electricity, be aware of the types of danger that can arise:

- burns and electric shock, which depending on the voltage can kill you
- faults in equipment or wiring, which can cause a fire
- electrical sparks from faulty equipment, which can cause flammable gas to explode.

Voltages

A range of voltages are used, depending on the equipment and circumstances.

In our homes, the usual voltage supplied for domestic appliances is 230 V, commonly referred to as 240 V. The difference in these two voltage figures is because voltages are referred to as 'nominal', which means that they can vary slightly.

230 V is often used in workshop environments to power hand tools and fixed machines. Protection for users is provided by a residual current device (RCD). This will disconnect the supply quickly if a fault or an unsafe condition occurs. Where heavier equipment or machinery is used, it may be necessary to use a 410 V supply, which you will hear referred to as 'three phase'.

On site, a lower voltage of 110 V is recommended, since lower voltages are safer. A piece of equipment called a transformer is used to reduce a 230 V supply to the safer voltage of 110 V.

Each voltage level is colour-coded, to make identification easier:

- 110 V – yellow
- 230 V – blue
- 410 V – red.

Wiring

Cables and wires need to be made of a material that is a good **conductor** of electricity. Copper wire is used as a conductor in the cable connecting a power tool to an electricity source. Three separate **insulated** wires are contained in an outer coating, and these are colour-coded as follows.

- The live wire is brown and conducts electricity to the power tool.
- The neutral wire is blue and completes the electrical circuit back to the power source.
- The earth wire is green and yellow striped and provides a path for the electrical current if the tool is faulty or damaged.

KEY TERMS

Conductor: a material through which electricity can flow freely

Insulated: covered in a material through which electricity cannot flow freely

▲ Figure 5.28 Colour-coded copper wires in a cable

When a plug is fitted to a cable, the colour-coded wires must be connected to the correct pins.

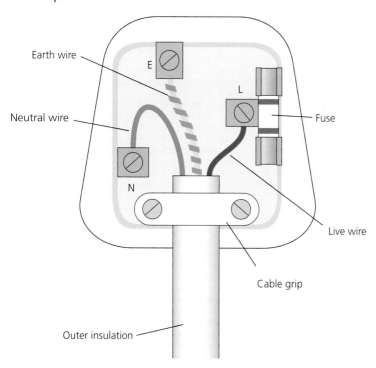

Earth wire

E

Neutral wire

L

Fuse

N

Live wire

Cable grip

Outer insulation

▲ Figure 5.29 A correctly wired plug

Safety precautions

Always check your power tools before use. If a fault is identified, inform a supervisor immediately. The tool will need to be repaired and should not be used. It should be removed from the work area, put in a secure location and clearly labelled 'Do not use'.

Always fully unroll an extension lead before using it. If you leave the cable coiled up during use, especially if it has a casing, it can overheat and cause a fire.

Study Table 5.9 to see the safety checks required when using electric power tools.

▼ Table 5.9 Safety checks on electric power tools

Item	What to check for	Action to take
Cables and plugs	Are there any signs of damage? Have they been repaired in the past? (Insulation tape may be hiding a damaged cable or plug.)	If there is any sign of damage, remove the tool from use until it is properly repaired.
Electricity supply leads	Are there any signs of damage? Have they been repaired in the past? (Insulation tape may be hiding a damaged supply lead.)	If there is any sign of damage, remove the tool from use until it is properly repaired.
	Are the supply leads creating a trip hazard?	Make sure that supply leads on the ground are protected from traffic or personnel crossing over them. If possible, use cable hangers to run supply leads overhead, out of harm's way.

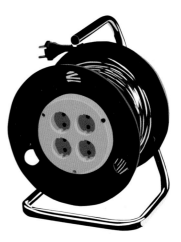

▲ Figure 5.30 Cable reel

▲ Figure 5.31 Cable protection

▼ Table 5.9 Safety checks on electric power tools (continued)

Item	What to check for	Action to take
Power-tool casings	Are there any signs of damage?	Plastic casings on power tools provide high levels of protection against electric shock when they are undamaged (this is often referred to as 'double insulated'). If a casing is cracked, the tool should not be used.
PAT sticker	Is the PAT sticker up to date?	PAT (portable appliance testing) is carried out by a trained and qualified electrician to check the safe electrical condition of tools and equipment. A sticker is placed on the tool after it has been tested. Tools that do not pass PAT must be taken out of use.

Battery-powered tools

Battery-powered tools are safer than mains-powered tools, since they operate at lower voltages. They are available in a wide variety of voltages, from 3.6 V for a small powered screwdriver all the way up to 54 V for more powerful drills and saws.

Although powered by a battery, these are still powerful pieces of equipment that can cause injury if not used with care. For example, a battery-powered drill produces a lot of **torque**, which can injure a worker's wrist and forearm.

ACTIVITY

Visit a tool supplier's website and search for battery-powered tools (they may be referred to as 'cordless'). List four different types and note the voltages.

Pneumatic tools

Tools powered by compressed air are known as **pneumatic** tools and are commonly used on building sites. Compressed air is used in:

- lifting equipment
- tools for compacting poured concrete
- tools for breaking concrete and masonry during demolition.

Misuse of compressed air can cause severe injury. Always follow safe working practices when using pneumatic tools and equipment.

- Wear appropriate PPE, such as hearing protection and safety glasses with side shields or goggles.
- Make sure all connections and couplings are secure and restrict hoses (sometimes referred to as 'bags') to avoid uncontrolled movement known as 'whipping'.
- Coil hoses carefully and hang them over a broad support when not in use. Hoses left lying on the floor can become damaged or cause a trip hazard.
- Never point the nozzle of an air hose at anyone or use compressed air to clean debris from a person's skin or clothing.

KEY TERMS

Torque: a force that causes rotation or twisting

Pneumatic: filled with or operated by compressed gas (air)

Fuel-powered tools

Fuel used to power tools on site is either diesel or petrol. Both of these types of fuel are combustible and can be hazardous when allowed to come into contact with skin.

When in use, fuel-powered tools produce exhaust fumes that are hazardous to health, containing high concentrations of carbon monoxide. This is a colourless, odourless gas that can cause death.

Follow these safety guidelines at all times.

- Never operate fuel-powered tools or equipment in an enclosed space.
- Wash hands thoroughly with plenty of soap after finishing work or any time when there is skin contact with fuel.
- Store fuel correctly in purpose-made containers, away from heat or flame.
- Use spill mats to avoid ground contamination when filling fuel tanks.

4.3 Plant and machinery

Construction sites can be busy places, with vehicles and machines moving around the workspace. For example:

- dumpers are used frequently for moving materials such as sand, soil, chippings and other aggregates
- cranes and forklifts are used to lift and position materials
- excavators are used to dig trenches and shape landscapes
- delivery vehicles are likely to be moving around the site regularly.

Vehicles

Contractors' personal transport should be accommodated on site. Parking areas should:

- be designated for private vehicles
- be separate from work areas
- have entry controlled by gates or barriers, with signs showing the entry procedure (such as a contact number for the gate operator)
- have walkways to and from them that are clearly segregated and fenced off from work areas.

Where the crossing of pathways and site vehicle routes cannot be avoided, there must be clear hazard signs to alert pedestrians and drivers to the potential dangers. Reversing vehicles are a major risk, and wherever possible the site should be laid out to avoid the need for reversing manoeuvres.

Storage areas should be designed to allow drive-through deliveries and collections if possible.

Lifting equipment

Many accidents are the result of untrained workers using equipment incorrectly. In the case of lifting equipment, lack of training and experience can lead to:

- cranes overturning
- materials falling from hoists
- failure of slings and chains.

ACTIVITY

Find the HSE booklet HSG150 online and download it. Read pages 54–62 onwards and list ways in which a site can be organised and arranged to reduce dangers from reversing vehicles.

▲ Figure 5.32 An overturned crane

INDUSTRY TIP

Build a good relationship with the operators of forklifts and cranes. You will not only improve the safety of transport operations, but you will also increase your productivity if you work well together.

▲ Figure 5.33 A fixed powered scaffold hoist

Operations using lifting equipment must be:

- carefully planned
- appropriately supervised
- carried out in a safe manner.

The workers performing each of these three tasks must be competent – that is, they must have the appropriate training, skills, knowledge and experience to perform the task safely.

All lifting equipment must have signs or labels attached to clearly show the safe working load (SWL), which must not be exceeded.

Excavators are sometimes used to lift and transport materials around site. Moving machinery poses a significant risk to workers on foot, since the design of the machine and the load being carried can create 'blind spots', meaning that the operator may not have a clear view around the machine. Always allow plenty of space between you and a moving machine; if possible, make your presence known to the operator and keep in their line of sight to maintain safety.

Fixed machinery

Machines such as cement mixers or powered scaffold hoists operate for extended periods in a fixed location. Construction machines are designed to handle heavy materials in tough conditions, so they are powerful pieces of equipment that must be treated with respect. Be continually aware of the dangers from moving parts.

Check that guards and other protection measures are in place and never operate a machine that is damaged or has parts missing. Report any damage or faults to your supervisor immediately and make sure the equipment is taken out of use.

4.4 Risks in construction and the built environment

Some work activities are known to involve higher levels of risk and must be managed with greater awareness and diligence to keep workers safe.

Confined spaces

Workers have died through lack of awareness of the dangers of working in confined spaces. Often those killed were rescuers trying to assist others in difficulty, but they were not properly trained or equipped to carry out the task safely.

Some confined spaces are easy to identify, such as enclosed tanks or sewers. Other are less obvious, such as deep excavations and even open-topped tanks.

Some confined spaces and the environment within them are naturally dangerous due to factors such as:

- gas build-up in sewers and inspection chambers
- gases leaking into trenches and pits in contaminated land such as old refuse tips
- rust inside tanks and vessels consuming oxygen
- liquids and slurries suddenly filing a space or releasing gases into a space when disturbed.

Some gases are invisible and heavier than air, so they form an unseen layer in the bottom of the confined space. A worker could be standing in a pool of gas without realising it. If they were to bend down with their head below the gas level, they could quickly fall unconscious.

The following basic precautions must be implemented to allow safe work in confined spaces.

- Make sure that workers have been trained to know the dangers and understand the required safety measures, including rescue procedures.
- Before entry, ventilate the space as much as possible, test the air inside the space and only enter if the test shows it is safe.
- Workers inside the confined space should wear rescue harnesses, with lifelines running to a point outside the confined space.
- Someone should be constantly outside the work area to keep watch and to communicate with workers inside.

The person outside the confined space must raise the alarm in an emergency. They should be competent to take charge of rescue procedures and use appropriate rescue equipment if it becomes necessary.

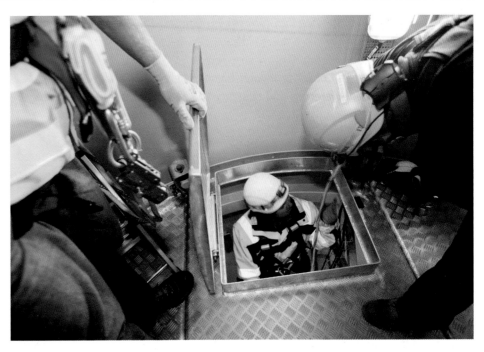

▲ Figure 5.34 A well-planned entry into a confined workspace

Underground services

Serious accidents have occurred when buried services have been damaged during excavation work. Without proper planning and appropriate precautions, workers risk injury to themselves and others in the work area. Furthermore, the interruption of services caused by accidental damage can lead to serious financial consequences for contractors and can create serious problems for consumers, especially those critically dependent upon them such as hospitals.

The route, extent and type of services adjacent to and crossing a site must be identified at an early stage of the construction project, whether working on new buildings/infrastructure or carrying out alterations or additions to existing developments.

▲ Figure 5.35 All service pipes and cables should be located before starting work on a project

Local authorities have drawings on file which identify boundaries, footpaths and roads surrounding the project site where services may be located. Guidance is available from the planning department of the local council through its online planning portal. Information about the location of services which can be confirmed prior to the start of works on site will be included on project drawings.

Service providers (or utility companies) often have their own information database from which locations of cables and pipe runs can be determined. Once gas and electricity services are located, their position must be marked, and permission to expose the services must be requested from the relevant provider.

Mechanical excavators and power tools should not be used near the indicated line of a service. Digging by hand should be done with the following points in mind.

- Hand-dig trial holes to confirm the position of the pipes or cables.
- If unidentified services are found, stop work until further checks can be made to confirm whether it is safe to proceed.
- Treat all pipes and cables as 'live' unless it is known otherwise. What looks like a rusty pipe may contain a live cable.
- Support service pipes and cables once they are exposed, to prevent them being damaged.
- Report any suspected damage to services.

Overhead services

As well as underground services, there may be overhead cables that must be considered during work on a development. Overhead electricity cables can be a hazard to operators of machines such as cranes and excavators as they operate and move about the site.

▲ Figure 5.36 Machinery such as mobile cranes can be at risk from overhead cables

If overhead services cannot be removed or rerouted, they must be clearly marked and measures must be put in place to signal to drivers of tall machines and vehicles that they are close to a hazard. These could include:

- erecting high-visibility barriers at least six metres away to prevent approach by site vehicles
- provide clearly marked crossing points beneath the lines at a height specified by the electricity supplier
- not storing materials in the area between the overhead lines and the ground-level barriers.

Working in trenches

Work requiring trenches or excavations must be carefully planned and carried out to prevent accidents.

Almost no type of ground will reliably support itself along the sides of an excavated trench or hole. One cubic metre of soil can weigh as much as one ton, so there is significant risk of injury to a worker caught in a collapse.

The need for adequate support will depend on the:

- type of excavation
- nature of the ground
- groundwater conditions.

Support for the sides of trenches and excavations can be provided using timber sheets, boards or steel trench sheet sections.

Specially designed systems such as trench boxes (sometimes referred to as 'strong boxes') do not require workers to enter the trench to install support.

ACTIVITY

Make a list of work tasks that must be performed in trenches or excavations. An obvious example would be installing pipes for drainage. Think of at least three more.

▲ Figure 5.37 Trench box system used to support the sides of an excavation

Any unsupported excavation will be safe only if its sides are sloped back (or 'battered') sufficiently or if the excavation is in sound rock. Edges of excavations should be protected with substantial barriers where people are liable to fall into them.

A competent person who fully understands the dangers and necessary precautions should inspect the excavation before workers are allowed to enter. Excavations should also be inspected after any event that may have affected their strength or stability, such as a period of heavy rain.

Working in unsafe buildings

When a building reaches the end of its useful existence, its condition may have deteriorated to such an extent that demolition is the only viable option. The structure may become fragile and unsafe to enter.

Demolition and dismantling are high-risk activities; workers can be injured falling from floor and roof edges or through openings and fragile surfaces. Contractors carrying out this type of work should possess technical expertise and be competent in a range of demolition methods.

<table>
<tr><td>**INDUSTRY TIP**</td></tr>
<tr><td>Never be casual about working in trenches or excavations. You might think a trench you worked in yesterday will be fine today, but get into the habit of inspecting it carefully yourself before each daily work session.</td></tr>
</table>

▲ Figure 5.38 Demolition of a multi-storey car park in the centre of Cardiff (note the dust-control measures)

Injuries to workers and the general public have also been caused by the premature and uncontrolled collapse of structures or parts of structures. It is best to consult a structural engineer when planning demolition to avoid this happening.

Key points to consider when planning safe demolition operations include the following:

- What is the age of the structure and what was its previous use?
- What construction methods and materials were used?

- Will the demolition sequence make the structure itself or any nearby buildings or structures unstable?
- Is temporary propping required?
- Are there still any live services? Gas, electricity, water and telecommunication services need to be isolated or disconnected. Where this is not possible, mark pipes and cables clearly so they are not disturbed during work.
- Can anyone not involved in the work be kept away by an exclusion zone around the work area? This should be clearly marked by barriers or hoardings.

When services to a building are no longer required for its operation, a process known as decommissioning takes place. This work should be undertaken by personnel who are trained and competent in safely identifying, isolating and protecting the installation that is to be removed.

Working with hazardous substances

The COSHH Regulations 2002 require the identification of:

- hazardous substances used on site
- processes on site that may produce hazardous substances.

The risks to site workers or members of the public must then be assessed and controlled.

Hazardous substances take different forms, such as powders, liquids or gases.

- Some substances give off harmful vapours/fumes, which can be inhaled (breathed in).
- Other substances are described as irritant or corrosive and can cause damage to the skin when it is exposed to them.
- Certain substances that can be injected, enter cuts in the skin or be absorbed through the skin are toxic (poisonous).
- Hazardous substances that are handled can leave deposits on the skin that can be transferred to the mouth when eating and then swallowed (ingested).

Carefully read the manufacturer's or supplier's safety data sheets provided for hazardous substances. These give information on how to safely use and store hazardous substances so that risks are minimised. Co-operate with your employer to establish and implement control measures when using potentially hazardous substances, such as **combustible** materials.

A hazardous substance that all construction workers should be aware of is asbestos. This is a durable fibre that was widely used in construction materials where resistance to heat was important and to give strength to cement products such as insulation boards.

Asbestos-related diseases kill more people than any other single work-related cause, both in the construction industry and in other occupations. All types of asbestos can be hazardous if disturbed. The danger arises when asbestos fibres become airborne, since they form a very fine dust which is often invisible.

KEY TERM

Combustible: able to catch fire and burn easily

▲ Figure 5.39 Safe storage of hazardous substances on site

Breathing in asbestos dust can cause serious damage to the lungs and cause cancer. There is no known cure for asbestos-related disease.

If you come across what you think might be asbestos when working:

- do not disturb the material
- stop work immediately
- inform your supervisor.

ACTIVITY

If asbestos is breathed in, it causes a disease that is often referred to as 'asbestosis'. Carry out research online and find out the symptoms. What other named illnesses are associated with this disease?

⑤ PRINCIPLES OF ENVIRONMENTAL PROTECTION

Construction activities have the potential to cause significant environmental damage and, for this reason, they have become the subject of increasing regulation. Significant progress has been made in managing and reducing waste, resulting in lower carbon emissions and less pollution.

5.1 Waste management and disposal

Many construction materials can be recycled or reused. Recycling can be supported if waste is carefully segregated (separated) into categories such as metal, wood, plastic and glass. For example, waste glass can be recycled into glass-fibre insulation for use in new buildings.

Prior to the adoption of environmentally friendly methods of managing waste, such as recycling, reusing and repurposing, most waste was disposed of by burying it in landfill sites or burning it at extremely high temperatures (incineration), depending on the type of material. Some waste is still disposed of in this way.

▲ Figure 5.40 Recycled glass can be used to make insulation

By recycling or reusing materials, overall carbon emissions that are produced during manufacturing can be reduced. Licensed companies are employed to safely dispose of hazardous waste such as contaminated fuel or oil, surplus resins and chemicals.

Proper disposal of waste on site is part of 'good housekeeping'. It protects the environment, reduces hazards and improves the image of the construction industry – no one who lives or travels near a construction site appreciates an untidy, dusty, polluting project or development which potentially will be ongoing for some time.

5.2 Pollution

There are three main types of pollution from construction activities:

- air pollution
- water pollution
- noise pollution.

In addition, because hazardous liquid chemicals are frequently used in construction, spillages can cause land pollution.

Air pollution

Air pollution can take the form of smoke, gases, fumes, dust and particles.

Machinery that is powered by fuels such as diesel and petrol produces exhaust gases and microscopic particles that can penetrate deep into our lungs. Well-maintained machinery will produce fewer pollutants. The use of fuel-powered machines should be limited and they should not be allowed to run unattended (idle) unnecessarily.

Fumes from paints and adhesives can also affect our lungs, leading to a range of health problems.

Water pollution

Water pollution can be the result of toxic substances finding their way into drains and watercourses, eventually affecting rivers and oceans. This type of pollution is often invisible, which can make it difficult to monitor.

When pollution has entered the water system, it can disrupt the ecosystem of animals, plants, bacteria and fungi, causing many species (including us) to suffer as a result.

Take care to prevent spillages when using paints, solvents and adhesives. Use spillage mats when filling the fuel tanks of powered machinery.

Noise pollution

Noise pollution can cause stress, sleep disturbance and, as mentioned previously, hearing loss if noise levels are high enough or prolonged enough. Research has also shown that noise pollution can affect the life cycles of animals and reduce their usable habitat.

Noise pollution can be reduced by:

- using silenced fuel-powered tools
- substituting quieter electric power tools for fuel-powered equipment
- not playing music loudly out of consideration for the wider community.

Test your knowledge

1 When a worker arrives on site for the first time, what type of meeting should they attend to learn about safety matters?

   a Introduction

   b Induction

   c Information

   d Interaction

2 What do the letters HSE stand for in connection with safety inspections?

   a Health and Standards Executive

   b Health and Safety Environment

   c Health and Standards Environment

   d Health and Safety Executive

3 What will the HSE issue when an unsafe activity on site must stop immediately?

   a An improvement notice

   b A prohibition order

   c An information notice

   d A postponement order

4 Which regulations specifically apply to the reporting of injuries?

   a RIDDOR

   b COSHH

   c PUWER

   d LOLER

5 Which legislation is specifically designed to protect workers from HAVS?

   a Control of Noise at Work Regulations 2005

   b Manual Handling Operations Regulations 1992 (amended 2002)

   c Control of Vibration at Work Regulations 2005

   d Provision and Use of Work Equipment Regulations 1998

6 In the workplace, what does it indicate if you have to raise your voice to have a normal conversation with someone two metres away?

   a You need to speak much louder

   b The other person is too far away

   c The other person is disinterested

   d You need to protect your hearing

7 Which document provides safety information about work situations where there is a high risk of accidents leading to major injury?

   a Bill of quantities

   b Schedule

   c Permit to work

   d Specification

8 Which type of safety sign is triangular and coloured yellow and black?

  a Mandatory

  b Prohibition

  c Caution

  d Supplementary

9 At what angle to the ground should a ladder be set?

  a 60°

  b 65°

  c 70°

  d 75°

10 Which part of a scaffold prevents objects from falling over the edge of the working platform?

  a Hand rail

  b Standard

  c Toe board

  d Putlog

11 What do the letters MEWP stand for?

  a Mobile elevated wheeled platform

  b Metal engineering work platform

  c Multi-engine wheeled platform

  d Mobile elevated work platform

12 Which voltage of electricity is used to make power tools safer on site?

  a 110V

  b 230V

  c 240V

  d 410V

13 Copper is a good material to use in electrical cables. This is because it is a good:

  a Conductor

  b Controller

  c Connector

  d Coupler

14 What colour is the live wire in an electrical cable?

  a Blue

  b Green

  c Brown

  d Yellow

15 What do the letters PAT stand for regarding inspection of electrical equipment?

  a Power appliance testing

  b Portable appliance testing

  c Power application testing

  d Portable application testing

Guided discussion

1 Explain why health and safety law is not just about punishing wrongdoers, but is also closely connected with the welfare of workers.

2 Explain how the CDM Regulations affect the welfare of people during the life cycle of a building.

3 Describe the importance of personal hygiene in maintaining good relationships on site.

4 Explain the difference between pressure and stress in the workplace. Give examples.

5 Under the Management Standards approach, what are an employer's responsibilities in taking care of a worker's mental health?

CHAPTER 6

EMERGING TECHNOLOGIES IN THE CONSTRUCTION AND BUILT ENVIRONMENT SECTOR

INTRODUCTION

Construction methods are always evolving, making use of innovative materials and computer-controlled work practices. These advances in **technology** have often happened over a relatively short period of time, but they have a huge impact on the built environment.

It is likely that the construction industry will continue to transform as new and improved materials and processes are adopted. In this chapter, we will look at emerging technologies and how they can lead to improved industry performance, better worker safety and greater protection of the natural environment.

KEY TERM

Technology: the practical application of scientific discoveries and knowledge

LEARNING OUTCOMES

By the end of this chapter, you will:
1 know about the use of Building Information Modelling (BIM)
2 know about emerging technologies and materials
3 know about off-site construction.

1 THE USE OF BUILDING INFORMATION MODELLING (BIM)

▲ Figure 6.1 BIM is used to manage the construction and operation of complex structures

Building Information Modelling (BIM) is a method of managing a construction project throughout a building's life cycle, from the design and planning stages through to demolition. While not in itself a computer program, BIM uses digitally processed information to analyse design elements of a building, including 3D modelling.

ACTIVITY

Search online for a free 3D-modelling computer program (hint – try SketchUp™). See if you can produce a simple house shape with a pitched roof. Be careful – these programs can be addictive!

1.1 Introduction to BIM

The design of a building begins with ideas and imagination. Not everyone is able to visualise a complete design after simply viewing a two-dimensional drawing. Using BIM, complex design ideas can be transformed into a visualisation that is easier for all personnel to work with.

BIM supports team co-ordination from the design stage through to the construction stage and beyond. It allows collaboration between every designer, engineer and contractor working on a project, providing comprehensive information about each other's workflow. This enhances the process of design and construction and allows exploration of alternative design possibilities even before work on site begins.

In the past, a problem such as the steel framing of a building interfering with the route of heating ducts could require extensive redrawing of plans and cause expensive delays. Using BIM, the internal building-engineering services of a structure can be revealed digitally to visualise the way they interact with each other. This allows the identification of clashes in systems ('clash detection') at an early stage in the design process.

ACTIVITY

Many modern restaurants and social venues have an 'industrial' design theme, where services at ceiling level are left visible. Next time you see this design approach, take note of the pipe and ductwork routes in relation to the surrounding structure and think how complex planning could be.

Once a design is finalised, construction of buildings and infrastructure can proceed with the confidence that the result will be truly fit for purpose. Decisions can be made on future operational maintenance of a building, so higher levels of efficiency and economy can be achieved throughout the building's life cycle.

The steps involved in this complex process could be simplified as the following steps.

1 Create the concept and formalise the **design brief**.
2 Refine and finalise the design.
3 Construct the design as specified.
4 Bring the design into use and operation.

By linking digital data and information with the realism of 3D modelling, a fourth 'dimension' can be added to the planning, design and construction processes. This allows the timescale and programming of a development to be modelled, so that projections of when materials, manufactured items and personnel are required can be examined and refined.

KEY TERM

Design brief: a working document that specifies what a client wants; it makes clear all the design requirements that designers will work to

IMPROVE YOUR ENGLISH

Search online for definitions of BIM, then write your own in 50 words or fewer.

1.2 Key terminology

BIM is a complex system designed to integrate the activities of multiple contributors to the construction process. Specialised terms and abbreviations are used to define the different elements of the system.

Common Data Environment (CDE)

The Common Data Environment (CDE) is a single central source of information used throughout a project. Relevant documents and data are brought together in a shared digital environment that can be accessed by all authorised personnel collaborating on a project.

The CDE typically contains schedules, contracts, registers, reports and **graphical** models. Large amounts of digital information can flow in a controlled way through the CDE during the development of a project, making it possible to reduce mistakes and avoid duplication.

Digital Plan of Work (DPoW)

While the CDE focuses on making documentary and graphical information readily available, the Digital Plan of Work (DPoW) provides details about:

- what is required
- when it is required
- who is expected to fulfil that requirement.

This means that everyone who consults the DPoW has a checklist that gives a clear idea of where they fit into the work programme.

Project Information Model (PIM) and Asset Information Model (AIM)

The Project Information Model (PIM) combines both graphical and non-graphical information for a construction project in a specific way, and this is stored and managed in the CDE.

The PIM is created during the development of the design brief and is progressively enhanced with increasing detail during construction. It provides an information 'history' through all stages of the project concerning designers, contractors and their suppliers. It becomes a virtual construction model of the building. This information is kept for future reference, to resolve any problems that might arise.

The Asset Information Model (AIM) is similar to the PIM, in that it combines relevant graphical and documentary information in an accessible digital format. The difference is that the AIM applies when the construction phase ends and, for this reason, it may include details of ownership and surveys related to the building's location. It provides information from the PIM about the 'asset' (the building) that is used to manage, operate and maintain the finished structure.

The stages managed by the PIM and AIM are designed to lead to a smooth, graduated handover of a construction project to the client or customer. There may be a defined period of aftercare that forms part of the design brief from the outset. This process is referred to as 'soft landing'.

Construction Operations Building Information Exchange (COBie)

To make sure that the huge amounts of digital information stored in BIM are consistent and accessible, the Construction Operations Building Information Exchange (COBie) was developed and continues to be refined.

The COBie concept is that all computer programs used in BIM should be written so that storage and editing of digital data conforms to a set format. This means that exchange of information between those involved in a construction project will be smooth and efficient, leading to improved performance on site.

Employer Information Requirements (EIR)

An Employer Information Requirements (EIR) document is produced within BIM to set out information required by the employer during the construction phase and for the operation of the completed building. The amount of detail it contains varies, depending on the size and complexity of the project.

The EIR may include:

- standardised methods for creating, naming and communicating information
- clearly defined role descriptions for those responsible for managing information
- a schedule identifying when information should be made available and who should have it.

BIM Execution Plan (BEP)

The BIM Execution Plan (BEP) links closely with the EIR and is produced at two stages in the project:

- before a contract is agreed (pre-contract)
- after a contract is signed (post-contract).

The pre-contract BEP demonstrates a prospective contractor's proposed approach to achieving successful completion of the project. It details the company's capability in terms of workforce capacity and proven competence.

The post-contract BEP is more comprehensive and sets out how information in the EIR will be provided by the contractor to support agreed targets for completion of the project and handover to the client. It contains details of roles and responsibilities of managers, key stages in the work programme, agreed procedures on working together and much more, making the contractor's role as an employer part of the **supply chain**.

BIM Protocol

A protocol is a set of rules that explain what course of conduct and procedures must be followed in specific situations. The BIM Protocol covers legal definitions that form part of a contract, concerning issues of responsibility, **copyright** and **liability**.

> **KEY TERMS**
>
> **Supply chain:** the sequence of activities required for a contractor to deliver a project
>
> **Copyright:** a legal right that gives an owner control over their work and how it is used
>
> **Liability:** the state of being legally responsible for something

ACTIVITY

The key terms discussed in this section are a fraction of those related to BIM that might be used during the construction process. Find an online glossary of BIM terms and see how many there are.

2 EMERGING TECHNOLOGIES AND MATERIALS

Many construction skills and work practices have been practically unchanged for centuries. However, the modern construction landscape is evolving, with the use of new materials and processes, and this progression is likely to accelerate as technology advances.

2.1 Introduction to 3D printing

3D printing is being used in more and more applications, ranging from dental and medical items to footwear.

It uses a computer-controlled machine that builds an item in three dimensions by **extruding** layers of material in a specified sequence, sometimes referred to as 'additive manufacturing'. The material used must harden rapidly as the layers are added.

3D printing can create:

- individual items with complex geometry
- complex moulds to produce multiple items repetitively.

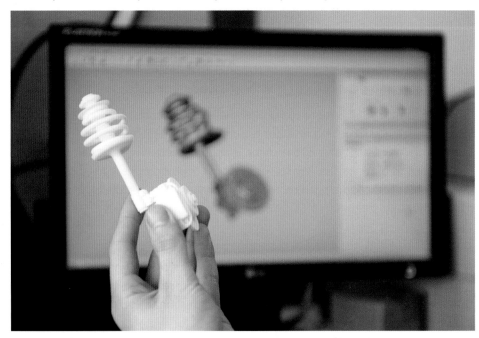

▲ Figure 6.2 3D printing can be used to produce items with complex geometry

In construction, 3D printing has been used to produce individual bespoke items such as decorative **cladding** panels and some structural components. In comparison with other manufacturing methods, this process can produce some items more cheaply and with virtually no waste.

Further development has shown the potential for this method to be used to 'print' entire buildings. Huge experimental printing machines, often with robotic

KEY TERMS

Extruding: forcefully squeezing material through a restricted opening in a controlled manner

Cladding: the application of one material over another to provide a skin or layer

arms, have been designed to create structures using specialist concrete with fibre additives. These machines can produce a finished structure relatively quickly and are able to work continuously around the clock if required.

The structures created so far using this system have shown that buildings can be produced with unusual and **organic** shapes, which do not conform to the traditional square or rectangular form. Building outlines can be attractively rounded, and internal rooms can have soft profiles without hard edges or corners.

KEY TERM

Organic: irregular and flowing in appearance

ACTIVITY

Look online for images of 3D-printed buildings. Which countries have already built experimental 'printed' buildings? Select an example you like and write down why you chose it.

▲ Figure 6.3 3D-printed buildings are being produced with unusual shapes and outlines

Printing a building is an enticing concept, and the structures produced using this method are often impressive in appearance. However, there are strong cultural links to buildings produced using traditional construction methods and there may be initial reluctance to accept buildings exclusively constructed using 3D printing.

IMPROVE YOUR ENGLISH

How would you feel about living in a 3D-printed building? Write a short account of your personal views about buildings constructed using traditional methods compared to those constructed using 3D-printing methods.

Building regulations will need to be developed to ensure that 3D-printed buildings are safe to use and durable. This will require experimentation and testing over a long period to establish suitable control measures.

2.2 Introduction to immersive technologies

'Immersive technology' describes systems that create a virtual world. In construction, it is used to create computer-generated designs of buildings or structures. Virtual models allow an audience not only to view the project externally in three dimensions, but also to feel as if they can enter and move freely within it, looking in any direction and seeing any content.

A simulated experience of moving within a structure is a powerful tool for creating and refining a building design. Design factors that would be difficult or impossible to examine in other ways can be explored extensively and any desired alterations can be made to a design before construction begins.

The process of assessing and evaluating a design during the planning stage of a project is called 'proof of concept'. Using immersive technology in this way can prevent expensive errors and increase efficiency and productivity. Examples of assessments and checks that can be made using this technology include:

- the effects of light and space within the structure
- the effects created by decorative surface finishes
- how the external landscape is seen from viewpoints within the building
- movement of occupants in open spaces and access to rooms
- fire safety and evacuation provisions.

▲ Figure 6.4 Immersive technology can be used to assess the effects of light, colour and viewpoints in a building at the design stage

Multiple users can enter this virtual world to collaborate on design decisions, making the process more creative and efficient. Often, a client will have definite ideas about how they want their project to be completed but may not be able to express their ideas clearly to designers. Using immersive technology, the designer can accompany the client using the virtual representation of the building to confirm that its proposed design fully matches the client's expectations.

Different types of immersive technology are used in various contexts.

Virtual Reality (VR)

The term 'Virtual Reality' is in common use and is often wrongly applied to every type of immersive technology.

A VR user is visually completely shut off from the outside world by wearing a head-mounted display (HMD). Whatever input the user sees through the HMD becomes their 'reality', allowing them to experience a digitally generated scene as if they were part of it.

The HMD senses user movement, so that when the user looks up, down or from side to side, the scene they see tracks their range of movement over 360 degrees to give the sense of looking around a space within the virtual building.

Augmented Reality (AR)

In Augmented Reality (AR), digitally generated images are superimposed over real-world images in real time. Instead of using an HMD, a device such as a smart phone or tablet can be used. This means that users are not completely shut off from the world around them.

HEALTH AND SAFETY

There are obvious safety considerations if a user cannot see their real-life surroundings while moving through a virtual environment. If you use a VR system, plan the way you use it with this in mind.

Many retailers have produced apps for mobile devices that use AR to allow a customer to 'see' how products would look in their home. For example, an item of virtual furniture can be placed in a potential customer's living space to see how it fits and looks, allowing an informed decision to be made before buying the real item.

AR could be used in construction to check how a new building, or an extension to a building, will appear in its intended location in relation to existing buildings. Internal installations such as kitchens or bathrooms can be superimposed onto the unfinished interior space to check that the designed layout will work.

▲ Figure 6.5 Verifying the final appearance of a kitchen layout using AR

Mixed Reality (MR)

Mixed Reality (MR) combines the VR headset approach with the AR method of overlaying a virtual image over a live image, so the user is not visually shut off from their surroundings.

The headset is more like a pair of glasses that allows the user to see the real world with a virtual image overlaid in their line of sight. As with VR, the headset senses the movement of the user and adjusts the overlaid image to align it with where it would exist in the real world.

▲ Figure 6.6 An architect using an MR system

Because of the similarity with AR in overlaying computer-generated images onto live views, MR is sometimes referred to as AR 2.0.

2.3 Evolving materials

The materials traditionally used in construction have proved durable and stable, sometimes over hundreds of years. However, the search for greater efficiency and long-term cost savings has led to the introduction of interesting and innovative materials that continue to find new applications in construction.

Many of these materials are the product of ingenious and imaginative scientific research and often in the first instance did not appear to have a use in construction. Let's look at some examples.

Graphene

Graphene is a one-atom-thick layer of carbon atoms arranged in a **hexagonal** pattern. It is the thinnest known material and is incredibly strong, and it is also an excellent conductor of heat and electricity. Interestingly, a related product is graphite, which is found in pencils.

KEY TERMS

Hexagonal: having six angles and six sides

Corrosion: the destruction of a material (usually a metal) by a chemical reaction caused by its environment

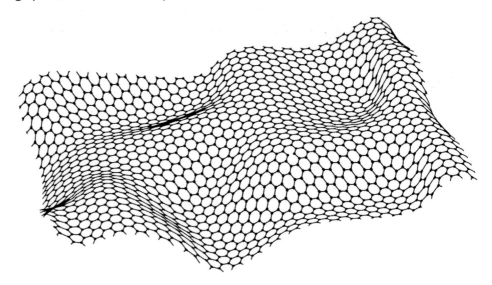

▲ Figure 6.7 Graphene has a hexagonal structure

Although graphene is extremely expensive to produce at the moment, it is finding a range of uses in construction, which will no doubt be extended as innovations and experiments continue. Examples include:

- surface coatings to protect steel components by preventing **corrosion**
- protective paints and liquid surface coatings to protect a building from the effects of water, cold and heat.

Other applications use graphene as a structural element to add strength to traditional materials. When added to concrete in specific ways, the strength of the concrete is increased significantly and it also becomes self-cleaning.

Graphene efficiently conducts electricity, which has led to experiments in producing spray-on solar panels. These could be easily applied to roof and wall surfaces. By eliminating the need for cumbersome units that are mechanically attached to buildings, installation of solar panels could become quicker and safer and offer an improved appearance.

Ventilation and heat-management materials

Porous materials have a range of applications in buildings, which may increase as building design evolves to become more energy-efficient. The control of heat transfer into and out of buildings, while providing adequate ventilation for the occupants, is now a critical consideration in building design. The targeted use of ventilated or porous materials in screens, filters and **baffles** can help to control the **thermal energy** of a building.

Ventilated building components manufactured from porous concrete or **ceramic** materials are being developed that act as heat exchangers. Some work by allowing air to be drawn from outside the structure through the tiny holes or channels in the material. Heat within the room that has already transferred into the wall material is picked up by the moving air to be transferred back into the room.

Research is ongoing to find the best methods of manufacturing these types of materials. Experimentation into the use of specialist substances referred to as 'phase change materials' (PCM) has produced construction components in the form of blocks, sheet materials and poured concrete.

KEY TERMS

Porous: having many minute holes through which air or water can pass

Baffle: a device that controls or restrains the flow of a liquid or a gas

Thermal energy: the energy a substance or system has due to its temperature

Ceramic: items manufactured from clay that is hardened permanently by being subjected to high temperatures

IMPROVE YOUR ENGLISH

Research how phase change materials work and write a short report. In what form are they integrated into construction materials to affect the heating and cooling of a building?

Liquid roofs

Innovative liquid roof-covering materials are easy to apply and offer waterproof finishes that are durable and attractive.

Traditionally, flat roofs have been covered using heavy felt sheet material laid in heated liquid bitumen. This has a limited lifespan, and application methods can be hazardous and messy and require a lot of specialist equipment. An alternative method involves applying a skin over the roof area, using glass fibre in a resin that hardens in a controlled chemical reaction.

New liquid roof materials continue to evolve, providing coverings that are applied cold and cure to form a seamless waterproof membrane.

Liquid-roof systems have several advantages.

- They are easier to apply to roofs with details such as drains, roof lights and complex geometry.
- They are easy and quick to apply using a brush, roller or spray.

▲ Figure 6.8 A finished liquid roof

KEY TERMS

Transparent: allowing light to pass through

Crystalline: having the structure and form of crystals or being composed of crystals

Fusing: combining or blending substances and materials by melting

Optically: by means of sight

- They retain flexibility, with good elastic properties over a wide temperature range.
- Moisture-triggered technology develops early rain resistance after application.

Installation of a liquid roof is a cost-effective method of making a new or existing roof waterproof. Depending on the coating system used, up to 25 years of reliable performance can be expected.

Typically, systems are installed with a primer coat, followed by two coats of liquid material (which includes a reinforcing fibre layer) laid in one operation. Advanced formulations continue to be developed, based on a range of materials.

Transparent aluminium

Aluminium is a chemical element. It is made into a lightweight metal that has long been used in the manufacture of items ranging from cooking utensils to aircraft parts. It is relatively soft, allowing it to be shaped easily, and it resists corrosion, which makes it useful for certain construction applications.

However, the development of '**transparent** aluminium' has caught the imagination of designers as a material that has the strength and durability of metal combined with the clear properties of glass. Transparent aluminium is not strictly metal, but a **crystalline** material formed by **fusing** aluminium with nitrogen and oxygen in precise amounts.

The resulting material is up to three times stronger than steel and is **optically** transparent. Using a material that is tougher, stronger and harder than glass could allow the construction of skyscrapers with transparent walls that require far less internal structural support. A building could have attractive 'glass' balconies and truly fire-proof windows.

ACTIVITY

Search online for 'transparent aluminium'. Find some images of items made from this amazing material. Work with another learner and list some ideas for ways this material could be used in construction.

▲ Figure 6.9 Transparent aluminium offers the possibility of constructing futuristic 'glass' buildings

This material is currently extremely expensive to produce, but if production costs can be reduced over time, other construction applications could include highly efficient heat-insulation materials, architectural heating panels, hardwearing decorative wall finishes and many more imaginative uses.

Self-healing concrete

Although concrete has high **compressive strength**, bending forces and **thermal movement** can create cracks in concrete components. If these cracks are not repaired, moisture can enter the concrete and cause further damage.

> **KEY TERMS**
>
> **Compressive strength:** the measured ability to resist squeezing or crushing
>
> **Thermal movement:** temperature changes causing something to expand or contract

▲ Figure 6.10 Tiny cracks in the surface of a concrete wall allow water to enter, causing damage over time

Self-healing concrete is an emerging material that uses several ingenious methods to automatically repair cracks, avoiding ongoing damage to the component. Many methods of achieving this have been researched and developed, including a project to explore new possibilities in which Cardiff University took a leading role.

One proven method uses limestone-producing bacteria. 'Bacterial concrete' uses a specific type of bacteria that become active when they come into contact with water or moisture. They can remain dormant within the concrete for up to 200 years; when activated, they use food sources and oxygen within the concrete to convert calcium into limestone. The limestone produced fills the cracks, preventing moisture from seeping into the surface.

Application methods being developed include sprays, which can be applied to existing concrete for repair of small cracks, and an additive included in the concrete mix before pouring. Since vast amounts of concrete are used worldwide, the potential for extending the life of concrete structures and minimising the expense of repairs by using self-healing concrete is extremely attractive.

3 OFF-SITE CONSTRUCTION

Off-site construction is the manufacture of parts or sections of a building away from the site location. The manufactured items are then transported to site, where they are assembled to complete the building. Off-site construction is often referred to as 'prefabrication' and may involve **modular construction** methods.

▲ Figure 6.11 Modules are constructed away from the site in factory conditions

Modules can be set up for use as specific rooms, such as bedrooms or kitchens. They can be produced with electrical wiring and plumbing already installed, allowing the finished structure to be assembled, and occupied, quickly.

3.1 Benefits of prefabricated construction

Off-site construction has been increasingly considered as a solution to many problems facing the construction industry. It can save time, improve safety and reduce waste, as well as improve quality.

Let's examine some of the benefits of prefabrication in more detail.

Sustainability

Shifting a large proportion of construction activities off site reduces the nuisance and disruption to communities near the project site. Less dust, less noise and lower **carbon emissions** are obvious environmental benefits, both to society on a local level and to the wider community.

Traditional building materials and methods are often not environmentally friendly. For example, concrete produces large amounts of carbon emissions during manufacturing and transportation. Modular construction can utilise low-energy manufacturing processes, using sustainable, eco-friendly and recycled building materials.

Components can be produced with increased accuracy using Computer-Aided Design (CAD), in conjunction with Computer Numerical Control (CNC) machines, which once set up can automatically produce identical components at speed. This can result in significant economic benefits and cost savings.

▲ Figure 6.12 CNC cutting machines can accurately and quickly produce components repeatedly

Value

Like most businesses, time is valuable in the construction industry. Prefabrication off site can speed up construction by reducing delays caused by poor weather conditions. A large proportion of the construction work is carried out in a controlled factory environment, so it is unaffected by the weather.

Factory conditions also mean that technical work can meet demanding production **tolerances** more easily. Automated production processes enhance quality at each stage of manufacture, leading to greater customer satisfaction.

Off-site construction benefits projects that require high volumes of component parts produced repetitively, such as housing developments. This type of large-scale mass production in controlled factory conditions can offer better financial value and consistent quality.

KEY TERM

Tolerances: allowable variations between specified measurements and actual measurements

▲ Figure 6.13 Off-site prefabrication can offer quality and value when used for housing construction

Efficiency

Prefabrication improves efficiency, since different critical stages of a construction project can happen simultaneously. For example, while modular sections of a structure are being assembled away from site in factory conditions, foundation and infrastructure work can be carried out on site at the same time. If unforeseen problems arise on site, since the off-site work is occurring in controlled conditions, some flexibility in work programmes can be accommodated.

▲ Figure 6.14 On-site preparation work can take place at the same time as off-site module assembly

By using a standardised design approach, large numbers of components can be manufactured efficiently with reduced waste. Production in controlled conditions, with operatives and machines working on clean level floors, also means that waste can be minimised. Accidental damage to materials can be reduced and cutting of materials can be carefully managed to reduce wasteful offcuts.

Large construction companies are working with government to invest significant sums in the development of off-site construction methods. Prefabrication reduces the reliance on skilled site workers who are in short supply, and this coupled with potential savings in time and cost are major drivers in the development process.

3.2 Types of prefabrication work

Older generations often have concerns about the label 'prefabricated', due to the low quality of mass-produced housing constructed after the Second World War to urgently provide homes. There is a perception that structures built using this method are of lower quality than conventional buildings.

Prefabricated construction methods developed in the 1960s to build high-rise apartment blocks were viewed as a major advance in providing cheap homes to tackle housing shortages. Unfortunately, due to unforeseen hazards affecting the design, a disastrous collapse occurred in a building in London, damaging the reputation of prefabricated construction in the minds of many.

Modern prefabricated buildings are far superior to historical examples. Advanced manufacturing systems and new technologies are used to produce buildings that are comfortable for the occupants, attractive to look at and sustainable. The development of different types of prefabricated buildings is ongoing.

ACTIVITY

1 Post-war prefabricated homes were commonly known as 'prefabs'. Visit https://museum.wales/stfagans/buildings/prefab to see what they looked like.
2 Research 'Ronan Point' online. Find out about the prefabrication methods used in this building and what went wrong.

Panelised systems

This system uses factory-made panels in the form of walls, roofs and floors. Because the panels are constructed in controlled factory conditions, they are produced to high standards of dimensional accuracy and parallel alignment.

The panel design is referred to as open or closed.

- Open panels are designed to have features like windows and insulation installed after delivery to site.
- Closed panels have doors and windows factory fitted and are fully insulated, needing little or no further on-site work to meet energy-efficiency standards.

Panels can be completed with internal or external finishes, removing the need for on-site skilled workers such as plasterers or tilers. Panelised systems offer design flexibility, since changes in design can be incorporated relatively easily. For example, different architectural features could be incorporated to offer variety in the appearance of similar buildings on a site.

Flat panels can be:

- stacked and transported relatively easily to site, offering cost savings
- easily lifted into position on site
- quickly secured together to form rooms within a structure.

Volumetric modular systems

'Volumetric' describes the method of joining large factory-finished modules, usually in the form of rooms such as living rooms and bedrooms, to make an almost complete building. The modules can be stacked on top of each other to produce multi-storey buildings within specified limits.

Engineering and technical services, such as plumbing and electrical systems, can be installed in the modules to higher standards during factory assembly than would be possible on site. Final connections are made when the building is fully assembled.

▲ Figure 6.15 Volumetric modules being lowered into position

This method produces a weather-tight structure in a relatively short timescale, reducing the reliance on good weather conditions to complete a project on time. Internal finishes (including wall tiles) and external finishes (including simulations of traditional finishes such as brick or stone) can be added during off-site production, reducing the reliance on skilled labour on site.

The process can be fast, efficient and precise, offering reductions in waste and supporting environmental values. The product can be standardised or customised to suit individual needs, creating the traditional housing arrangements of detached, semi-detached and link housing and apartments to suit the design brief.

However, because of the bulkiness (or volume) of each module, transport may pose difficulties that must be planned for, potentially adding to costs.

Hybrid systems

Hybrid systems essentially combine panel and volumetric systems.

- A building may be designed to use the panel system for most of the structure, where rooms such as bedrooms have the minimum of detail and functional features. The panels are attached to a frame system, which can be constructed using concrete, steel, timber or a mix of all three.
- Other special-purpose rooms, such as bathrooms and kitchens, are manufactured as complete modules, sometimes referred to as 'pods', with all high-value plumbing items installed ready for on-site connection. These units are secured within the structural frame alongside the panel units to complete the layout of the building. Pods may also be used to upgrade existing buildings.

Sub-assemblies and components

As mentioned previously, panel units can be produced to form walls, floors and roofs. They can be described as 'sub-assemblies' when they become structural units in themselves.

▲ Figure 6.16 A roof sub-assembly being lowered into position

Prefabricated components such as stairs, dormer windows and chimneys may be integrated into wall, floor or roof sub-assemblies to speed up the construction process on site. In addition to sub-assembly panels, sub-assembly modules manufactured from a range of materials have been developed for fast installation in a structure while maintaining long-term durability.

▲ Figure 6.17 A prefabricated dormer window

For example, modules for special-use rooms such as bathrooms must be designed to resist potential damage from water over time. The range of materials used for this specialist application could include a hybrid combination of steel for the shell of a pod, concrete to form a rigid base for a wet-room application, and glass-reinforced plastic (or polymer) to provide waterproof surfaces.

The whole precision-made assembly, including items such as ceramic tiles, vinyl floor finishes and plumbing, can then be lifted into position for final connection within the main structure.

▲ Figure 6.18 Bathroom pods installed at an early stage of construction in an apartment block

Test your knowledge

1   When using BIM, what does 'clash detection' mean?

   a   Identification of site vehicles that have been involved in accidents

   b   Identification of incorrect equipment that has been delivered to site

   c   Identification of where decisions of one manager are different to others

   d   Identification of building design parts that will interfere with each other

2   Which working document specifies exactly what the client wants?

   a   Work concept

   b   Design brief

   c   Work protocol

   d   Data brief

3   At what stage in a project does the Asset Information Model (AIM) apply?

   a   When planning permission is given

   b   When the site is being prepared

   c   When the design brief is being written

   d   When the construction phase ends

4   What do the letters EIR stand for in BIM terminology?

   a   Electrical Information Regulations

   b   Employee Identification Regulations

   c   Employer Information Requirements

   d   Engineering Information Requirements

5   Which term is used to describe the process of 3D printing?

   a   Sequential manufacturing

   b   Additive manufacturing

   c   Extruded manufacturing

   d   Subtractive manufacturing

6   Which type of immersive technology uses a headset to visually shut off the user from their surroundings?

   a   Augmented Reality

   b   Virtual Reality

   c   Mixed Reality

   d   Simulated Reality

7   In what pattern are the atoms in a sheet of graphene arranged?

   a   Hexagonal

   b   Octagonal

   c   Heptagonal

   d   Pentagonal

8 When managing heat transfer, what do the letters PCM stand for?

    a Physical control measures

    b Phase change materials

    c Periodic control methods

    d Partial cooling modules

9 What are Computer Numerical Control (CNC) machines used for?

    a To calculate the total cost and spending of a project

    b To control the movements of cranes and diggers on site

    c To automatically produce identical components at speed

    d To produce a work programme that shows times and dates

10 Which construction method involves fitting together factory-made room modules on site to create a building?

    a Panelised

    b Volumetric

    c Specialist

    d Traditional

Test your knowledge answers

CHAPTER 1

1 d – Infrastructure
2 b – Domestic
3 c – Semi-detached
4 a – Era
5 d – After the mid-twentieth century
6 b – Commercial
7 b – Cultural
8 c – Trunk roads
9 c – Suspension
10 b – Revetment

CHAPTER 2

1 d – To contribute to the smooth running of the project
2 c – Conservation and repair
3 b – Contractor
4 c – Carpenter
5 b – Electrical, plumbing and carpentry
6 c – Civil engineer
7 a – Plumbing
8 b – Consultant
9 d – The brickwork has been jointed or pointed properly
10 a – It is known for its ability to let structures 'breathe' which helps to reduce damp

CHAPTER 3

1 d – Theodolite
2 a – Grey water
3 b – By removing the need to cut components
4 b – Block plan
5 c – Approved Documents
6 a – Pad
7 b – More than 10°
8 c – Continuity of work
9 b – Planned or preventive
10 b – Implosion

CHAPTER 4

1 c – Higher National Certificate
2 d – Architect
3 b – Levy
4 b – General operatives
5 d – You want an employer to clearly see your employability
6 b – Being determined to do a job well
7 a – Overheads
8 b – Invoice
9 c – Networking
10 b – Bankruptcy

CHAPTER 5

1 b – Induction
2 d – Health and Safety Executive
3 b – A prohibition order
4 a – RIDDOR
5 c – Control of Vibration at Work Regulations 2005
6 d – You need to protect your hearing
7 c – Permit to work
8 c – Caution
9 d – 75°
10 c – Toe board
11 d – Mobile elevated work platform
12 a – 110 V
13 a – Conductor
14 c – Brown
15 b – Portable appliance testing

CHAPTER 6

1 d – Identification of building design parts that will interfere with each other
2 b – Design brief
3 d – When the construction phase ends
4 c – Employer Information Requirements
5 b – Additive manufacturing
6 b – Virtual Reality
7 a – Hexagonal
8 b – Phase change materials
9 c – To automatically produce identical components at speed
10 b – Volumetric

Improve your maths answers

PAGE 63

14 700 ÷ 420 = 35

PAGE 123

Money in £15 150.50; Money out £12 550.00; Bank balance £14 600.50

Glossary

Aesthetic: concerned with beauty and good taste; relating to the appreciation of beauty

Aggregate: material in the form of grains or particles, such as sand, gravel or crushed stone

Approved Code of Practice (ACOP): a set of written directions and methods of work, issued by an official body or professional association and approved by the HSE, that provides practical advice on how to comply with the law

Aqueduct: an artificial channel in the form of a bridge carrying water across a valley

Architrave: the shaped or moulded timber trim surrounding a door frame

Area: the space occupied by a flat shape or the surface of an object

Artifacts: ornaments or other objects made by humans that are of cultural or historical interest

Assets: items of value owned by a company

Attenuation ponds: storage ponds that manage storm water by releasing it slowly

Baffle: a device that controls or restrains the flow of a liquid or a gas

Bankruptcy: a legal process to deal with a person or business that is unable to repay outstanding debts

Bespoke: purpose-made for a particular customer

Biodiversity: all the different kinds of life in one area

Biomass: organic matter used as a fuel, such as wood products, dried vegetation, crop residues, aquatic plants and even rubbish

Cantilever: a projecting beam or structural member supported only at one end

Carbon emissions: carbon dioxide released into the atmosphere; scientists believe this is a cause of climate change

Ceramic: items manufactured from clay that is hardened permanently by being subjected to high temperatures

Cladding: the application of one material over another to provide a skin or layer

Classical: following a traditional and long-established style; terms such as 'classical Greek' can be applied to architecture

Climate change: a large-scale, long-term change in our planet's weather patterns and average temperatures

Combustible: able to catch fire and burn easily

Combustion: the process of burning something, such as fuel

Compacted: firmly packed or pressed together

Compensation: something (usually money) awarded to someone in recognition of loss, suffering or injury

Compressive force: pressure against an object that causes it to become squeezed or squashed

Compressive strength: the measured ability to resist squeezing or crushing

Conductor: a material through which electricity can flow freely

Conservation and repair: the process of bringing a building or structure back to its original state

Consultant: an expert who provides advice professionally

Contractor: a person or company that agrees legal terms (a contract) to provide a paid service

Conventions: agreed, consistent standards and rules

Copyright: a legal right that gives an owner control over their work and how it is used

Corner bead: a strip of formed sheet metal placed on the outside corners of walls to protect the plastered edge

Corrosion: the destruction of a material (usually a metal) by a chemical reaction caused by its environment

Crystalline: having the structure and form of crystals or being composed of crystals

Cultural: connected with the customs, ideas and behaviours of a society

Curing: the process of a material becoming hard by cooling, drying or crystallisation

Datum: a fixed point or height from which reference levels can be taken

Demolition: when something (such as a building) is torn down and destroyed

Design brief: a working document that specifies what a client wants; it makes clear all the design requirements that designers will work to

Detached properties: stand-alone buildings that do not share any walls with other properties

Dressed stone: natural stone that has been cut and shaped to the required size, shape and finish

Ducts: enclosed tubes, passages or channels for conveying liquid or gas

Ecosystem: a community of living organisms that interact with each other in a specific environment

Elevation: a view of the front, back or sides of a building

Embodied energy: the total energy required by all the activities associated with a production process. The carbon this process produces is sometimes referred to as 'embodied carbon' or 'capital carbon'

Era: a period of time distinguished by particular characteristics

Ethic: structured rules about behaviour, based on what is accepted as right and wrong

Extruding: forcefully squeezing material through a restricted opening in a controlled manner

Fabric of a building: the structure or framework of a building

Fall: the specified angle of slope between two points

Fibrous: containing or consisting of fibres

Footings: the section of masonry from the concrete foundation to the ground-floor level; sometimes, the whole foundation is referred to as 'footings'

Fossil fuels: natural fuels such as coal, oil and gas, formed from the ancient remains of living organisms

Friction: the resistance that one surface or object encounters when moving over another

Functional: designed to be practical and useful, rather than attractive

Fungus: organism that feeds on organic matter such as wood

Fusing: combining or blending substances and materials by melting

Galvanised: coated with a protective layer of zinc to prevent rusting

Graphical: relating to visual information or computer graphics

Gypsum: a soft white or grey mineral used in the manufacture of plaster

Heritage skill: a skill handed down from the past

Hexagonal: having six angles and six sides

Humidity: a measurement of the amount of water vapour or 'wetness' in the air

Induction: an occasion when someone is introduced to and informed about a new job or organisation

Infrastructure: the basic systems and services that a country or organisation needs in order to function properly

Insulated: covered in a material through which electricity cannot flow freely

Invert level: the bottom of the inside of a drainage pipe within an inspection chamber

Joists: parallel timber beams spanning the walls of a structure to support a floor or ceiling

Kinetic: relating to, caused by or producing movement

Legislation: a law or set of laws made by a government

Levy: a payment you are obliged to make to an official body or organisation

Liability: the state of being legally responsible for something

Linear measurement: the distance between two given points along a line

Live: carrying an electric current

Load-bearing: supporting the weight of a building or parts of a building above

Medieval: relating to the Middle Ages, a time period from about the fifth century to the late fifteenth century

Modular construction: combining factory-produced, pre-engineered units (or modules) to form major elements of a structure

Nominated: chosen by name for a particular job

Optically: by means of sight

Organic: irregular and flowing in appearance

Percentage: part of a quantity expressed in hundredths

Percussion tools: power-driven tools which operate by striking rapid blows

Personal protective equipment (PPE): all equipment (including clothing affording protection against the weather) which is intended to be worn or held by a person at work and which protects against one or more risks to a person's health or safety

Perspective: in drawing, a way of portraying three dimensions on a flat, two-dimensional surface by suggesting depth or distance

Philanthropist: a person who benefits others, especially by the generous donation of money to good causes

Plan view: a view from above a building; a 'bird's eye' view

Plant: machinery or equipment used for an industrial application

Pneumatic: filled with or operated by compressed gas (air)

Porous: having many minute holes through which air or water can pass

Prime costs: payments that cover work undertaken by nominated sub-contractors, nominated suppliers and statutory undertakings

Profit: the difference between the amount earned and the amount spent when buying, operating or producing something

Rafters: beams set to suit the angle of the roof pitch, forming part of its internal framework

Ratio: the amount or proportion of one thing compared to another

Redundancy: a form of dismissal from a job when employers need to reduce the size of their workforce

Reinforced: strengthened or supported with additional material

Renewable: from natural sources or processes that are replenished or replaced

Renovation: the process of repairing and improving a building to return it to good condition

Repurposing: adapting for new uses while retaining valuable features

Reservoir: a large natural or artificial lake used as a source of water supply

Ridge: the highest horizontal line on a pitched roof where sloping surfaces meet

Scale: when accurate sizes of an object are reduced or enlarged by a stated amount

Scrim tape: a strip of open-weave fabric used to strengthen joints between plasterboards

Segregate: set apart, isolate or separate

Semi-detached properties: two buildings joined together on one side by a shared (party) wall

Semi-permeable membrane: a thin sheet of material that allows only certain substances (such as water vapour) to pass through it

Specification: a detailed description of the materials and working methods that must be used for a project

Statutory undertakings: the various services that are brought to the site, such as water and electricity

Storm water: water from heavy falls of rain or snow, or ice melt, that is not absorbed through the surface of the ground

Sub-contractors: workers or companies employed by a contractor to do part of a job

Subsidence: a gradual sinking or downward movement of material beneath a building

Supply chain: the sequence of activities required for a contractor to deliver a project

Technology: the practical application of scientific discoveries and knowledge

Tensional force: the force created by pulling something from either end

Terraced properties: similar buildings joined together in a row by the side (or party) walls

Thermal energy: the energy a substance or system has due to its temperature

Thermal movement: temperature changes causing something to expand or contract

Tolerances: allowable variations between specified measurements and actual measurements

Toolbox talks: short meetings arranged at regular intervals at your work location on site to discuss safety issues; they are used to give safety reminders and inform personnel about new hazards that may have recently arisen, for example, due to extreme weather

Torque: a force that causes rotation or twisting

Transparent: allowing light to pass through

Trunking: a cover used to hide and protect electrical wires in a building

Trussed rafters: factory-assembled timber components that create the slope of a pitched roof

Undulation: a wavy form or outline

Viaduct: a long bridge structure, constructed as a series of arches, carrying a road or railway across a valley or depression in the landscape

Voltage: the amount of potential energy between two points in an electrical circuit, expressed as volts or V

Volume: the total space in three dimensions taken up by an object, material or substance

INDEX